The Prediction Birthday Book

The Prediction

BIRTHDAY BOOK

Joan Revill and Jo Logan

BLANDFORD PRESS
POOLE · DORSET

First published in the U.K. 1984 by Blandford Press,
Link House, West Street, Poole, Dorset BH15 1LL.

Copyright © 1984 Triad

Distributed in the United States by
Sterling Publishing Co. Inc.,
2 Park Avenue, New York, N.Y. 10016.

British Library Cataloguing in Publication Data

Revill, Joan
The prediction birthday book.
1. Horoscopes
I. Title   II. Logan, Jo
133.5′4   BF1728.A2

ISBN 0 7137 1443 3

Typeset by Poole Typesetting (Wessex) Ltd.

Printed in UK by Butler & Tanner Ltd, Frome & London.

Contents

Introduction

At one time it was considered usual to keep a book in which to record birthdays. Such a book served a double purpose: it acted as an aide-memoire – in much the same way that we use wall-planners nowadays to help remember significant dates – but it was also a permanent memento of the individuals whose birthdays it contained.

Falling somewhere between a diary and a scrapbook, friends and relatives were invited to contribute to its contents. Some wrote a few words, perhaps a saying or short verse composed especially for the occasion, others executed a small sketch against their birth dates.

Sometimes the birthday book itself had appropriate sayings printed under the dates and was decorated with line drawings of plants or trees associated with the months or zodiacal signs. For many of these books were in fact astrological: the year was divided not into calendar months but into periods corresponding to the Sun signs.

This birthday book is laid out in a similar way and, as the astrological year starts with Aries, the first sign of the zodiac, the first date in it is March 22 when the Sun usually enters that sign. Following tradition, each date is accompanied by written material, in this case some of the famous people whose birthdays coincide with the dates.

As an additional bonus, each sign is prefaced with a short description of the general characteristics of the twelve zodiacal signs, as well as the 'correspondences' – numbers, days, colours, stones, etc. – associated with each of the Sun signs.

The ancients taught that astrology was one of the keys to discovering the purpose of life and accorded certain characteristics to each of the luminaries and planets that influenced life on Earth. Each of these celestial bodies was also awarded rulership over one or more of the zodiacal signs which are, in fact, those constellations through which the Sun, Moon and planets apparently pass in their journey across the sky. Thus those people born under a particular sign will share some of the characteristics of the planetary body that influences that sign.

The Sun, without which there would be no life, is the driving force behind the whole of our solar system and denotes will-power, vitality, leadership, creativity and the urge to achieve. In astrological terms, it rules, governs or strongly influences the royal sign, Leo.

The Moon reflects the light of the Sun at night and represents the subconscious, instinct, habit, imagination and the emotions. It rules the sign Cancer and is associated with birth, motherhood, the home and family, also new ventures and experiences.

Mercury, the messenger of the gods, is associated with the intellect: the power of communication, perception, interpretation, intelligence, reason and self-expression. This is one of the planets that rules more than one sign – in this case Gemini and Virgo.

Venus, the planet of love, beauty and harmony, also governs two signs – Taurus and Libra. It is associated with partnerships, affection, the arts, adornment and the social graces. Venus is also the planet of wealth and relates to material possessions and money.

Mars, the god of war, denotes passion, desire, energy, courage, initiative, assertiveness and is associated with martial activities. It has rulership over the sign Aries and, traditionally, Scorpio (more recently attributed to Pluto) and can be regarded as co-ruler of that sign.

Jupiter, known as the greater benefic, is the planet of expansion. It rules Sagittarius and, by tradition, is co-ruler of Pisces. It represents the higher mind and is associated with wisdom, education, speculative thought, optimism, spontaneity, philosophy, religion and benevolence.

Saturn, the planet of old age, has rulership over Capricorn and, by tradition, is co-ruler of Aquarius. It denotes tradition, convention, stability, perseverance, tenacity, responsibility, justice, restriction, limitation and self-discipline.

Uranus was 'discovered' in 1781 and represents the unexpected or the unusual and is strongly associated with sudden or disruptive changes. It signifies inspiration, originality, inventiveness, independence and eccentricity. It is co-ruler of Aquarius.

Neptune, discovered in 1846, is named after the god of the sea and denotes the limitless boundaries of space. It is the planet of intuition and imagination and is associated with idealism, illusion, mystery, compassion, sympathy and inspiration; it is co-ruler of Pisces.

Pluto, the 'newest' planet (1930), is named after the god of the underworld and represents the subconscious mind and subtle or hidden influences. It signifies transformation, regeneration, transmutation, reinforcement, intensification; it is co-ruler of Scorpio.

Many factors must be taken into consideration before an accurate character assessment can be made. Yet Sun sign astrology can give a general indication of a person's nature so, with the help of the characterisations and information given for each of the Sun signs, together with hints offered by the personalities of the well-known figures mentioned in this book, you may achieve a greater understanding of yourself and others.

If nothing else, it could be fun to see who of the famous shares your birthday and that of your friends and family . . . Happy Birthday!

Aries

22 March – 20 April

Aries, the first sign of the zodiac, is ruled by fiery Mars, the planet named after the god of war. The warrior instinct is usually displayed by Arien people as a form of courage, or bravery, and their disregard for danger is an easily discernible character trait.

Ariens are born fighters who come straight to the point, no messing about, even if this does win them the reputation of unnecessary bluntness. They also like to be number one, the first or the best, for Aries personifies the pioneering spirit. Unfortunately, in order to meet this desire they may become rather pushy or bossy.

Yet there is nothing underhand, complex or secretive about these fundamentally honest people. Aries is an uncomplicated sign: it's the young man's sign and has all the young person's qualities and defects. It stands for energy and aggression; typical Ariens are speed mad and live violently, fearing only disease, old age and death.

Life is regarded as a challenge and Ariens have a natural talent for working their way to the top, whether in sports or at work. They are good at recognising their own particular abilities and will exploit these to the full in order to achieve their goals. Usually, they will make an early start in a career; very few leave it to middle age to get started on the ladder in their chosen occupation.

Ariens have great initiative and an infectious enthusiasm for all they do, so have all the earmarks for success whether they decide to enter politics or the world of sport, start a business, found a movement, join the Forces, become surgeons or whatever. And if they don't win their way to the top, it won't be for the want of determination, drive or competitiveness.

These dynamic, enterprising, quick-witted individuals are quite prepared to work hard in order to achieve the status they desire. Honest and straightforward themselves, they will expect the same honesty in others and any form of double-dealing is totally unacceptable to the Arien nature. Of course, they will expect the best and, although prepared to pay for it, will haggle a bit if they think there is a chance of striking a better bargain. After all, Ariens do enjoy a challenge!

Their fervent, impetuous drive is infectious; their self-sufficiency and faith in the loyalty of others is irresistible.

Although rather inclined to use rush tactics, there is no meanness in the Arien nature and they are as generous in emotional matters as they are in material things, so their marriage prospects are good.

There may, though, be a few storms and tempests to weather on the way to the altar because Ariens are very impulsive and inclined to fall in love at first sight. So these passionate and demonstrative individuals do need to look before they leap into marriage which will satisfy their strong – but rarely admitted to – romantic streak.

Full of fun and enthusiasm, Ariens make exciting, warm and lively companions in any situation. Sometimes impatient, overbearing and arrogant, at others brave, quick-witted and adventurous, Ariens can never be accused of being dull! They are, after all, the children of Mars and the pioneers of the zodiac.

ARIES

Planetary Ruler   MARS
Element/Quality   FIRE/CARDINAL
Keywords   ENERGY, AGGRESSION, INITIATIVE, ACTION
Day   TUESDAY
Number   9
Colour   BRIGHT REDS
Metal   IRON
Stones   DIAMOND, GARNET, BLOODSTONE, RUBY
Countries   ENGLAND, DENMARK, GERMANY, PALESTINE,
PARTS OF POLAND
Places   In Britain: BLACKBURN, BIRMINGHAM, LEICESTER, OLDHAM
Elsewhere: BURGUNDY, CRACOW, FLORENCE, MARSEILLES, NAPLES,
PADUA, VERONA
Trees/Shrubs   HOLLY, HORSE CHESTNUT, MONKEY PUZZLE,
THORN, FIR
Flowers/Herbs   GERANIUM, GINGER, NETTLE, PEPPER,
POPPY, THISTLE

22 A good start for Aries. Birthday boy **Roger Whittaker** (1936) sings his *New World in the Morning*.
Lady Dowding is an Arien force to be reckoned with. She founded *Beauty Without Cruelty* back in the days when nobody cared.
Stephen Sondheim (1930) wrote the lyrics for bloodthirsty *Sweeney Todd*.

23 Some lively birthdays to remember today. Water speed king **Donald Malcolm Campbell** (1921) and first 4-minute miler **Roger Bannister** (1929) race by at 276.33 mph and 15 mph respectively while engineer **Wernher von Braun** (1912) eclipses them both. He invented the rocket and made the space age possible.

24 **Malcolm Muggeridge** (1903), journalist, lecturer, interviewer and self-confessed Christian Anarchist. Like many Ariens (show-offs!) was attracted by the stage and made a convincing Gryphon in Jonathan Miller's *Alice*.
Virile **Steve McQueen** (1930), *The Cincinnati Kid*. Hoodlum **Clyde Barrow** (1909), Public Enemy No 1. He died, messily, with friend Bonnie.

25 **Gloria Steinem** (1934) US feminist. Founded *Ms* magazine and Women's Active Alliance. **Anita Bryant** (1940), nearly Miss America 1959, recorded religious albums and led the Save Our Children anti-homosexual crusade.
Elton John (1947) is a fitness freak.
Conductor **Arturo Toscanini** (1867) was the 'wrath of God' on the rostrum.

26 The plays of **Tennessee Williams** (1911) – *Streetcar Named Desire, Cat on a Hot Tin Roof* – are raw red meat, served up quivering. Horrific themes, although probably all in a day's work for **Charles Wheeler** (1923) TV foreign correspondent. *His* astrological twin is that good, 'straight' novelist **Elizabeth Jane Howard.**

27 **Frederick Royce** (1863) of Rolls Royce started in a small way making dynamos. An Arien exception, he perfected the *silent* engine but was typical enough to suffer a breakdown from overwork. Another human dynamo – the tiny, temperamental actress **Gloria Swanson** (1898). Actor **Michael York** (1942). Singer **Sarah Vaughan** (1924).

28 **Michael Parkinson** (1935) presents his interviewees: **Dame Flora Robson** (1902), **Dirk Bogarde** (1920), **Richard Stilgoe** (1943); plus Labour leader **Neil Kinnock** (1942). As his hobbies include association football he should have something in common with his sports-mad host who wrote *Football Daft* and a biography of George Best.

29 **Margaret Howard** has on her 'Pick of the Day': controversial politician **Norman Tebbit** (1931); controversial journalist **Chapman Pincher** (1914); controversial TUC leader **Jack Jones** (1913); controversial composer **Sir William Walton** (1902) whose *Facade* music caused outrage; and uncontroversial composer **Richard Rodney Bennett** (1936) who wrote the score for *Murder on the Orient Express*.

30

Goya (1746) dallied and duelled and painted the gruesome *Disasters of War*. **Van Gogh** (1853) painted in violent swirls of colour and went mad. **Anna Sewell** (1820) was 'never burdened with fear' and *Black Beauty* throbs with her revolutionary zeal. Still with us: **Rolf Harris** (1930) and **Warren Beatty** (1937).

31

David Steele (1938) a formidable politician and Liberal party leader. Likes fast cars. Quote: 'Not as nice as he looks!'
John Fowles (1926), brilliant intellectual. His novels, *The French Lieutenant's Woman*, etc., burst on the scene to enormous acclaim.
Actor **Richard Chamberlain** (1935) of *Dr Kildare* and *Shogun*.

1

Appropriately, top clown **Sid Field** (1904) was born on April Fool's Day. So was **Cicely Courtneidge** (1893) – Ivor Novello wrote *Vitality* for her.
At the piano **Zes Confrey** (1895) goes into action with his frantic *Dizzy Fingers* and *Kitten on the Keys*.
At the dictaphone, thriller writer **Edgar Wallace** (1876).

2

Penelope Keith has a houseful of awards; so has **Sir Alec Guinness** (1914).
Hans Christian Andersen (1805), despite the fairy tales, was a toughie with an awful temper. **Catherine Gaskin** (1929) writes gothic romances.
Casanova (1725) had his full share of Arien virility and romance. **Jack Brabham** (1926) raced cars.

3

Twins for 1924, **Marlon Brando** and **Doris Day** (her story revealed a life as dramatic as her films).
Tony Benn (1925), né Anthony Wedgwood Benn, darling of the left.
Vivian Nicholson (1936), the big Pools winner, whose motto was 'Spend! Spend! Spend!' She ended up broke – and went on the stage.

4

Yesterday's tophole writer for lads, **Mayne Reid** (1818) – *The Scalp Hunters,* etc. – lived adventurously in the Wild West and as a lieutenant/reporter in the Mexican War.
Syd 'Cyanide' Cooper (1945) wrestles anyone.
Arthur Murray (1895) opened a chain of dancing schools and the foxtrot can be lethal!

5

Dramatic actress **Bette Davis** (1908) 'twins' writer **Mary Hemingway,** the wife of Ernest so she had to be tough.
Actors **Gregory Peck** (1916) and **Spencer Tracy** (1900). 'Aren't you too short for me?' asked Katherine Hepburn. 'I'll soon cut you down to size,' he answered – and did.

6

Actor **Walter Huston** (1884) introduced us to *September Song,* which isn't seasonable but never mind. He was the father of film director John Huston. Then there's **Butch Cassidy** (1866) with or without the Sundance Kid, ebullient conductor **Andre Previn** (1929), comedian/magician **Paul Daniels** (1938), and another actor **Peter John** (1943).

7

TV reporter **Martyn Lewis** (1945) has been everywhere and done everything.
David Frost (1939) appears to be unstoppable and is now a tycoon.
Billie Holliday (1915) is every jazz musician's favourite singer with a tender-rasping voice.
And **Andrew Sachs** (1930), alias Manuel, turns up to spill the birthday sherry.

8

Isambard Kingdom Brunel (1806), English engineer and Titan of the early days of railways and steamships. Never slept, smoked cigars incessantly. Died of overwork.
Feminine counterpart **Mary Pickford** (1893) billed as the World's Sweetheart. Don't be fooled. Under the golden curls was a powerhouse of business acumen. **Ian Smith** (1919).

9

Playboy Emperor **Hugh Hefner** (1926) aims at a 'healthy, positive interest in sex' and his Bunny girls have made him a packet. **Charles Baudelaire** (1821) wrote *Les Fleurs du Mal* which, in those days, got him tried for blasphemy.
Valerie Singleton (1937) of *Blue Peter* is a nice, adventurous Arien.

10

A noisy birthday. **William Booth** (1829), founder and first General of the Salvation Army, and **Harry Mortimer** (1902) couldn't appear without a band or two in attendance, but no doubt **Gloria Hunniford** (1940), **Norman Vaughan** (1927), **Omar Sharif** (1932) and your friends can hold their own.

11 **Edward Sylvester Ellis** (1840) pioneered the American 'dime' novel. Specialised in Red Indians, bear hunters, trappers and cowboys. Author of *Pony Express Rider, Blazing Arrow, Captured by Indians.*
Colonel Caine VC (1906) and **Commander Charles Lamb** (1914), author of *War in a String Bag,* have known quite lively times too.

12 **Jeremy Beadle,** self-styled 'Curator of Oddities' is himself collected for our *Today's the Day* Birthday Book. His companions are French multiple-murderer **Landru** (1869) who lost his Arien head under the guillotine, **Lionel Hampton** (1913) jazz vibraphonist, drummer and bandleader, energetic, volatile, gregarious, and playwright **Alan Ayckbourn** (1939).

13 **Richard Trevithick** (1771), engineer, man of action and 'dretful scoler', built the forerunner of Stephenson's railway engine. The idea was like 'maney other wild fanceys that flyes through the brain.' Had an adventurous life, made a fortune but died a pauper. A fate which did not befall **F. W. Woolworth** (1852).

14 Political Ariens: **'Papa Doc'** (Francois Duvalier) (1907) who presided over a regime of terror in Haiti, and **Bishop Muzorewa** (1925) of Zimbabwe.
Erich von Daniken (1935), Swiss writer of best-seller, *Chariots of the Gods?,* postulated the theory that ETs once visited the earth.
John Gielgud (1904), a commanding actor.

15 **Jeffrey Archer** (1940) once ran for Britain in the 100 metres but had enough breath left to enter politics (youngest MP in the House) and to write best-sellers like *Kane & Abel.*
Joe Davis (1901) world champion snooker player for 20 years. Tough, aggressive, self-assured and unbeatable.

16 Comic geniuses **Charlie Chaplin** (1889), **Spike Milligan** (1918) and **Peter Ustinov** (1921).
Author **Kingsley Amis** (1922), whose *Lucky Jim* in 1954 introduced a new sort of hero, was one of the original 'angry young men'. Very socialist in youth but has moved to the right.

17 **Henry Kelly** (1946) has his own birthday Birthday Guests – lone yachtswoman, the intrepid **Clare Francis** (1946), now a TV personality and novelist; jazz trombonist **Chris Barber** (1930) and bandleader **James Last** (1929). Plus **George Adamski** (1891) who claimed to have observed and travelled in flying saucers and caused more apoplexy than anyone.

18 **Hayley Mills** (1946) made her first film when she was 12. **Wilbur Wright** (1867), American aviation pioneer. Effervescent composer **Franz von Suppé** (1819).
Clarence Darrow (1857), famous American defence lawyer who was violently opposed to capital punishment yet thought the noblest death was on the battlefield, so Aries is vindicated.

19   **Dudley Moore** (1935). Lack of inches and poor health spurred him to stardom. Crime writer **Gladys Mitchell** (1901) and her sleuth, Mrs Bradley. **Jayne Mansfield** (1932) super-ego actress and sportswoman, was decapitated in an accident in 1967. Hasty Aries is apt to lose its head, although seldom so literally!

20   Technically, **Hitler** (1889) and **Harold Lloyd** (1893) were Taureans, although both seemed Ariens. Lloyd lost part of his hand in an explosion but held on by two fingers to the tops of skyscrapers and never used a stuntman. TV's **Paul Heiney** (1949) and **Peter Snow** (1938) have exciting lives too.

NOTES

Taurus

21 April – 21 May

Determined, practical and reliable, Taureans are very security conscious. Usually rather staid in their attitudes and ideas, they need stability, both at home and at work. Any sudden changes in either can upset them, so they are reluctant to take risks, even when it is necessary.

Although they lack flexibility, Taureans have strong emotions, are quite sensitive and can be extremely generous, both with their money and their affections. While on this delicate subject, Taureans have sexual stamina and are faithful lovers but can be very possessive – of people as well as things – a trait that can, and often does, lead to jealous outbursts although they are normally slow to anger.

Patient, trustworthy and very loyal, they expect the same loyalty from their partners and simply will not tolerate their loved ones paying court to another man or woman. But, once convinced that their chosen mate belongs to them, and them alone, they make kind, reliable, affectionate partners and their marriage prospects are excellent for they are probably the most faithful of all the signs.

If all this sounds a bit dull, don't you believe it! Taureans have a rich, sensual enjoyment of life; they appreciate good food, wine and luxurious surroundings – and have the determination and business acumen necessary to ensure they acquire them. Traditionally ruled by Venus in her more practical aspect, Taurus is a creator of beauty yet Taurean artists and artistes won't starve in garrets; however airy-fairy their calling, they keep an eye on their bank balances.

But not all Taureans are luxury seekers, they can derive great pleasure

18

from the simple, natural things of life too. Many people born under the sign of the Bull enjoy gardening, country walks, horse-riding and generally being out in the open air. In fact, many a Taurean is quite happy to plod along for hours outdoors; and he/she can probably do with the exercise because, like the bull, Taureans tend to put on weight, especially after middle-age.

The sign of the physically and mentally strong, Taurus traditionally rules the throat which is the weak spot but which, conversely, produces the beautiful or distinctive Taurean voice and many singers are born under this sign. So, too, are painters, dancers, writers, musicians and . . . accountants!

Music and maths often go together and Taureans who don't make it to the concert platform are good bankers and financiers . . . good administrators and organisers too. Slowly but surely they accumulate power and money; steadily they build up financial empires. So, wealthy folk and founders of family fortunes number in the Taurean ranks, not that they are stingy with their money, quite the reverse; materialism is prevalent, but so is generosity.

Another characteristic of the sign is humour, not corrosive wit but light-hearted fun. This trait, coupled with Venusian charm and sex appeal has benefited many a Taurean performer who might otherwise have been stampeded from the glamorous world of entertainment. Not that there would have been any resentment on the Taurean side, in any case, because the overriding characteristic of this sign has to be kindliness.

TAURUS

Planetary Ruler   VENUS
Element/Quality   EARTH/FIXED
Keywords   PATIENCE, DETERMINATION, CONSERVATION, LOYALTY
Day   FRIDAY
Number   6
Colour   GREEN, CREAM, MADONNA BLUE
Metal   COPPER
Stones   EMERALD, CORAL, LAPIS LAZULI, JADE
Countries   CYPRUS, EIRE, IRAN, ASIA MINOR
Places   In Britain: ASHTON-UNDER-LYNE, DUBLIN
   Elsewhere: LEIPZIG, LORRAINE, MANTUA, PALERMO, PARMA, RHODES,
   ST LOUIS
Trees/Shrubs   ASH, ALMOND, APPLE, HAZEL
Flowers/Herbs   DAISY, DELPHINIUM, FOXGLOVE, HAREBELL,
   MINT, ROSE

21

H M Queen Elizabeth II (1926) heads the birthdays. She is very rich and a country-woman at heart. Business-like and shrewd but feminine.
Norman Parkinson (1913) fashion and royalty photographer is obviously at home in this sign of beauty.
Charlotte Brontë (1816), 'a quiet, thoughtful girl,' according to Mrs Gaskell.

22

Violinist **Yehudi Menuhin** (1916) of whose playing Albert Einstein said, 'You have once again proved to me that there is a God in Heaven.'
Kathleen Ferrier (1912) was as lovely as her rich, creamy contralto; unaffected, humorous, affectionate, generous, a good cook and amateur artist.

23

St. George's Day. Traditionally the birthday of **William Shakespeare** (1564). The Bard knew all about the Bull for, 'Were we not born under Taurus?' demanded Sir Toby Belch when calling for revels and cakes and ale.
Also **J. M. W. Turner's** birthday (1775), an uncouth character yet his paintings are 'tinted steam'.

24

Entertainers **Shirley Maclaine** (1934) and **Barbra Streisand** (1942).
Authors **Anthony Trollope** (1815) – thick, solid, satisfying, very English books – and **Elizabeth Goudge** (1900). Like Trollope has a penchant for cathedral town settings – *A City of Bells, The Dean's Watch*.
Clement Freud (1924) knew we were coming and baked the birthday cake.

25 **Walter de la Mare** (1873). No poet more loved, more evocative or haunting. Wrote of enchanted landscapes, twilights dim with rose; beautiful ladies of the west countree; travellers who came knocking and old women who went blackberry picking, along the hedges from Weep to Wicking. By profession, an accountant!

26 Nelson's **Lady Hamilton** (1765) was beautiful, sweet and sexy but grew fat through 'guttling' and – disgrace to Taurus – died destitute. **Anita** *(Gentlemen Prefer Blondes)* **Loos** (1893) could have told her that 'kissing your hand may make you feel very very good but a diamond and sapphire bracelet lasts forever.'

27 **Ludwig Bemelmans** (1898) wrote and illustrated children's books – notably *Madeline* – but also worked in various restaurants including the Ritz which he described in *Hotel Splendide*.
Anglo-Irish Poet Laureate **Cecil Day Lewis** (1904) had, to quote his wife Jill Balcon, 'one of the most spellbinding voices I ever heard.'

28 Philanthropist **Lord Shaftesbury** (1801). His appropriate Taurean memorial is Eros, the god of love, in Piccadilly Circus. 'A kind of amiable bull in a china shop of good intentions,' wrote Dickens. Took on, single-handed, the dark, Satanic mill owners, master sweeps and donkey beaters. Strong, affectionate character.

29

Two conductors to superintend today's rendition of *Happy Birthday to You!* **Sir Thomas Beecham** (1879) and **Sir Malcolm Sargent** (1895). Plus **Duke Ellington** (1899) and **Lonnie Donegan** to jazz it up a bit if need be.

For the moneybags, **William Randolph Hearst** (1863) multi-multi-milllionaire newspaper proprietor.

30

Super-rich ex-**Queen Juliana** of the Netherlands (1910) can enter appropriately to the *Gold & Silver Waltz* of **Franz Lehar** (1870). He made his fortune with *The Merry Widow* and was a canny businessman. 'Down-to-earth, calm, regular, without ecstacies, fury or despair.' A ladies' man.

1

Actresses **Una Stubbs** (1937) and **Joanna Lumley** (1946). The former trained as a dancer, the latter took a modelling course. **Kate Smith** (1909), a well-known singer in the States. Called the *Songbird of the South*, although a somewhat rotund songbird. Used to sing, *God Bless America!* to enormous acclaim.

2

Jerome K. Jerome (1859), author of *Three Men in a Boat*, said it was impossible to enjoy idling unless one had plenty of work to do. **Bing Crosby** (1901) made millions through his apparently lazy style. **Dr Benjamin Spock** (1903) has been a Taurean haven for distraught parents for decades.

3

Boxers **Sugar Ray Robinson** (1920) and our own **Henry Cooper** (1934) were born today, also **Mrs Golda Meir** (1898), ex-PM of Israel who, in her prime, looked capable of knocking both their heads together.
Coming out strongly under Venus, master perfumier **Francois Coty** (1874) and singer **Englebert Humperdinck** (1936).

4

Lucy Walker (1907), popular Australian novelist. Her countryside is the outback, her heroes the impossibly gorgeous station owners! Playing the heroine, **Audrey Hepburn** (1929). **Thomas Lawrence** (1769) would doubtless have painted her if their eras had coincided.
Comedian **Terry Scott** (1927) once studied accountancy.
Rich matador **El Cordobes** (1936).

5

Taurus is the money sign and born today in 1818 was the earnest German philosopher and socialist **Karl Marx.** His literary monument is *Das Kapital,* a diatribe against capitalism. However, champion jockey **Sir Gordon Richards** (1904) didn't do so badly from the system! Neither did the beautiful **Empress Eugénie** (1826).

6

Sigmund Freud (1856), psychoanalyst, invented sex.
Rudolph Valentino (1895) personified it and featured in countless female fantasies of the 20s. 'Catnip to women!'
Another actor, **Orson Welles** (1915). His bulk and affluent look proclaim the successful Taurean. Adores bullfights and was quite an aficianado himself – well, this *is* Taurus.

7 **Dr Edwin Land** (1909) invented the polaroid camera. He's very rich but has worked hard. 'My whole life has been spent trying to teach people that intense concentration for hour after hour can bring out resources that they didn't know they had.'
Birthday mates, **Brahms** (1833) and **Robert Browning** (1812).

8 Naturalist **David Attenborough** (1926), famous for his *Zoo Quest* programmes and *Life on Earth* series. An expert on world wild life. After reading or seeing *Jaws* by **Peter Benchley** (1940) one isn't, perhaps, so keen on the wild life kick and turns thankfully to soprano **Heather Harper** (1930) for soothing!

9 **Barbara Woodhouse** (1910) was an agricultural student, then trained horses in Argentina and 17,000 dogs all over the place (except in the compiler's locality, alas). In 1979 was TV personality of the year.
Jolly **Joan Sims** (1930) of the *Carry On* films, laughs at anything – including herself.

10 Dancer **Fred Astaire** (1899) – 'The luckiest hoofer and luckiest guy in the world!'
Gorgeously funny **Arthur Marshall** (1910) who seems to have had a pleasant life of it.
Sir Thomas Lipton (1850), Scottish merchant and philanthropist, once owned the world's largest chain of shops.
Monica Dickens (1915), author, country and animal lover.

11 Salvador Dali (1904) – his moustachios resembled the glyph for Taurus! Weird Dali landscape reveals actress **Margaret Rutherford** (1892), puzzled but game; comedian **Phil Silvers** (1911) in the bearskin overcoat, leopardskin golfing cap and ocelot neckerchief he affected; choreographer **Martha Graham** (1893) limbering up; and jazz cornetist **Joe 'King' Oliver** (1885).

12 Two great English drolls: **Edward Lear** (1812) and the 'Lad' himself, **Anthony Aloysius St John Hancock** (1924). Lear is surrounded by Jumblies, Pobbles, Owls, Pussy Cats and innumerable Old Men and Young Ladies ostensibly from Tonga and Riga, but as native to our shores as the Unfortunate Person of Cheam.

13 **Joe Louis** (1914), world heavyweight champion for 11 years, made a fortune but was finally floored by the Revenue.
Sir Arthur Sullivan (1842) was a charming man, perfect foil for his irascible Scorpion opposite, W. S. Gilbert. Lived luxuriously.
Country-loving novelist **Daphne du Maurier** (1907), author of *Rebecca*.

14 **Phil Drabble** (1941), TV's professional countryman. Mainly known as presenter of *One Man and his Dog, In the Country* and *Living World*. Has written many books on country topics and natural history. A rustic day. Even comedian **Eric Morecambe** (1926) cites birdwatching as a hobby. Although one wonders. *Bird* watching?

15 **Michael Balfe** (1808) composed the opera *The Bohemian Girl* (who dreamt she dwelt in marble halls). 'A blue-eyed, handsome little fellow, the very embodiment of sunny smiles and laughter.' Sang his own compositions in society drawing rooms and did very well. Fashion photographer and astute businessman **Richard Avedon** (1923).

16 **Liberace** (1919) with his piano, sequins and candelabra, **Richard Tauber** (1891) singing *You Are My Heart's Delight,* exemplify Taurus's talent for commercialising its artistic gifts. **H. E. Bates** (1905) painted luscious word pictures of the English countryside in *The Darling Buds of May.*
Jesters **Bernard Braden** (1916) and **Roy Hudd** (1936).

17 **Robert Smith Surtees** (1803), a wealthy landowner with strong views on agriculture and a genius for creating English comic characters like Taurean Mr Jorrocks, a wealthy grocer, nearer 20 'stun' than 18, whose hunting exploits are recorded in *Jorrock's Jaunts & Jollities.* For the tally-ho's, horn player **Dennis Brain** (1921).

18 **Pope John Paul II** (1920) plus a well-known Catholic **Norman St John Stevas** (1929). He was formerly Minister of Arts which opens the floodgates for ballerina **Margot Fonteyn** (1919), singers **Ezio Pinza** (1892), **Boris Christoff** (1918) and **Perry Como** (1912), pianist **Clifford Curzon** (1907) and actress **Holly Aird** (1969).

19
Comedienne **Victoria Wood** (1953). Suave-voiced interviewer/compere **David Jacobs** (1926). **Dame Nellie Melba** (1859) sang like an angel but was, disconcertingly, a stout lady with sound commercial instincts.
Our first woman MP was American **Lady Nancy Astor** (1875). She was immensely rich and the bluntest, most bullying woman ever.

20
Musician: **Hephzibah Menuhin** (1920).
Actor: **James Stewart** (1908).
Artist: **Henri Rousseau** (1844) painted primitive, exotic landscapes as in *Le Lion afflamé*.
Author: **Honore de Balzac** (1799). Of peasant stock and looked it. Obsessed by the financial status of his characters. Everything in his books is compressed, solid and material.

21
The Sun moves from Taurus to Gemini now so your friends can be of either, or both, persuasions, so can **Desmond Wilcox** (1931) – one invariably adds, 'Esther Rantzen's husband'; **Malcolm Fraser** (1930), Australian PM; **Raymond Burr** (1917) alias Perry Mason, and the lovable, over-sized music man **Fats Waller** (1904).

NOTES

Gemini

22 May – 21 June

Gemini, the sign of the Twins, is ruled by Mercury, the winged messenger of the gods, and is associated with all forms of communication. Those of this sign must meet people and go places; they are the live wires, versatile, witty, urbane, very intelligent, brittle and unsentimental.

Fun people who don't like routine and find it difficult to concentrate on one subject for any length of time, Geminians talk fast, think fast and aren't above pulling a fast one or two either! Not that they are malicious, far from it, but they do enjoy exercising their mental agility and are prone to fantasise, to exaggerate and . . . to lie.

Of course, such traits might be more usefully employed in writing film, TV or stage scripts and there are many Geminians who earn a living doing just that because writing is second nature to them. Others enter the information services and become newspaper men or women, reporters, broadcasters, lecturers and teachers (being so childlike themselves, they get on well with children).

Geminians are superb garnerers and distributors of facts: their rag-bag minds are always on the look-out for new things; new people, places and gadgets (they are gadget mad!). The trouble is their staying power – or lack of it! Like children, they get bored very quickly and their lively curiosity is soon caught by something even more novel.

So they travel widely, are great party-goers and givers, sociable, friendly, communicative, full of fizz and sparkle . . . and a bit slapdash and superficial. They tend to be here today, gone tomorrow – a trait that has earned them the reputation of being flirts. This accusation isn't really accurate although it is true that many Geminians do marry more than once.

Gemini is a dualistic sign and many of its subjects manage to run two homes and/or two jobs simultaneously and successfully. They are often bi-lingual, too; they have a gift for languages and are very quick to learn. Often this talent fits in well with their desire to travel, to discover more about other countries and cultures, to explore the unknown: Geminians are perpetual students.

The keyword is versatility: the true Geminian can turn his or her hand or, more accurately, mind to almost anything – and probably will. Although they will not actively seek extra money or prestige in their careers, no Geminian despises money. Not that they want money in order to indulge in the luxuries of life, but simply because it enables them to participate in their various interests and activities: it buys them freedom.

Bright and adaptable, Geminians usually find it easy to make money although, unfortunately, it often slips through their fingers nearly as fast as it comes in. So, despite their ability to think up money-making schemes, they get into just as many financial scrapes as the rest of us and, as money itself is valueless to them, will quite happily spend their last fiver on a book, record or cinema seat for a friend – or give it to a stranger.

Generous, spontaneous, charming and vibrant personalities, these sons and daughters of Mercury make delightful and amusing companions . . . but you need wings on your feet, too, to keep up!

GEMINI

Planetary Ruler   MERCURY
Element/Quality   AIR/MUTABLE
Keywords   COMMUNICATION, VERSATILITY, CURIOSITY,
   CHANGEABILITY
Day   WEDNESDAY
Number   5
Colour   SHARP YELLOW, BLACK & WHITE COMBINED
Metal   PLATINUM/ALUMINIUM
Stones   PERIDOT, BERYL, CHRYSOLITE, ONYX
Countries   ARMENIA, N.E. AFRICA, BELGIUM, USA, WALES
Places   In Britain: LONDON, PLYMOUTH, WOLVERHAMPTON
   Elsewhere: BRUGES, NEW YORK, NUREMBURG, MELBOURNE,
   SAN FRANCISCO, VERSAILLES
Trees/Shrubs   LABURNUM, NUT BEARERS, ELDER
Flowers/Herbs   ANISEED, BITTERSWEET, FERN, FORSYTHIA,
   HARESFOOT, HONEYSUCKLE, JASMINE

22 Kenny Ball (1931) trumpeter, and **George Best** (1946) footballer, are particularly mobile Geminians.
Laurence Olivier (1907) has been described as two-faced, a split personality, going from Mr Puff to Oedipus in the same evening.
Arthur Conan Doyle (1859), the creator of Sherlock Holmes, 'possessed no capacity for dullness.'

23 Actress **Joan Collins** (1936), screen's top sex symbol 1979, and a writer as well. Several marriages, children and stepchildren. Hobby – giving parties. **Douglas Fairbanks** (1883) was a wow at parties. He was a swashbuckling hero on stage and off. 'An unconscious harlequin' . . . 'A sort of Ariel' . . . 'An overgrown schoolboy'!

24 Surprisingly **Queen Victoria** (1819) was Geminian. Before marrying Albert she was a giddy, dancing miss and even when monumental retained Gemini's gift for words, writing diaries, letters and *Leaves from our Highland Journal*.
Bob Dylan (1941) sings his own songs of social comment and doubtless supports Polish **Lech Walesa** (1931).

25 Beverley Sills (1929), world's highest paid opera star, began career when 3 in soap opera and singing commercials. Great fun and rattles on amusingly for hours.
Lord Beaverbrook (1879) newspaper proprietor and 'fixer'. Mischievous. Some liked, some loathed him. Reporters **Caroline Dempster** (1955), **Tina Jenkins** (1958).
Jazz virtuoso **Miles Davis** (1926).

26 Dimunitive **George Formby** (1904) was professional jockey when only 10. Went on stage with his banjolele and 'me daft little songs.' Light, fast, saucy. So is **Sheila Steafel** (1935)! Actor **Robert Morley** (1908) is too stout really to fit into Gemini but lists his hobbies as conversation and horse-racing.

27 Airy Gemini demands freedom of movement. Tall, graceful **Isadora Duncan** (1878), exponent of classical dance, wore only light draperies. No underclothes or shoes or stockings. **Amelia Bloomer** (1818) had her ideas too on constricting dress and advocated the use of the unfortunate garment which now bears her name.

28 **Ian Fleming** (1908), creator of James Bond, was tall, thin, restless, widely-travelled, gadget-mad, fabulously intelligent, witty and, of course, a newspaperman. A true Gemini. He was easily bored and, in the end, was even bored with success. Sunshine moods alternated with moroseness.
Thora Hird (1913) is *all* sunshine!

29 President **John F. Kennedy** (1917) lived at a breakneck pace and had a curious, enquiring mind.
G. K. Chesterton (1874), although elephantine in appearance, juggled with words like a maniac conjurer.
On stage: **Beatrice Lillie** (1898) sophisticated comedienne, **Bob Hope** (1903) master of the quick one-liner.

30 Two TV **Peacocks,** reporting, announcing and presenting – **Sue** (1952) and **Chris** (1945) and *his* twin, actor **Norman Eshley. Aleksei Leonov** (1934), Soviet cosmonaut, first man to step from his ship into space.
Much-married jazz clarinetist **Benny Goodman** (1909) was the first white bandleader to popularise the uncompromising jazz style.

31 The name of **Heath Robinson** (1872) still describes a particular type of crazy but workable machine. **Prince Rainier** of Monaco (1923) loves gadgets and practical jokes.
Clint Eastwood (1930) personifies the tall, rangy, sinister, anti-hero cowboy but is a keen motor-cyclist. So is actor **Denholm Elliott** (1922).

JUNE

1 Jet pioneer **Sir Frank Whittle** (1907) propels everyone off to a flying start. There's the always young **Marilyn Monroe** (1926); **Colleen McCullough** (1937), author of *The Thorn Birds;* **Gemma Craven** (1950) who, at 3, won a singing contest, and **Bob Monkhouse** (1928) who, at 15, sold jokes to Max Miller.

2 Actor **Alan Dobie** (1932) has played everything from pantomime cat to Macbeth taking in Sergeant Cribb *en route.* Newscaster **Leonard Parkin** (1929) has roved and reported from all over the world.
Sir Edward Elgar (1857) composed *Cockaigne,* the old name for Cockney, and Cockneys, like New Yorkers, come under Gemini.

3

Quicksilver **Anita Harris** (1942), another Gemini who started young (3) and has won many awards.
Artist **Raul Dufy** (1877) developed a calligraphic style and in a few scratchy lines could present lively race-tracks, casinos, esplanades.
Raul Castro (1931), brother of Fidel himself. **Allen Ginsberg** (1926) leader of the Beat Generation.

4

Robert Merrill (1917) one Geminian half of that constantly requested duet from *The Pearl Fishers*. As he hasn't his usual partner here's Italian mezzo-soprano **Fedora Barbieri** (1920). Off stage she's sociable, full of fun and charming.
Artist, specialising in cherubic tiny tots, **Mabel Lucy Attwell** (1879).

5

Novelist **Margaret Drabble** (1939) confesses to a fear of being socially cut off.
Ivy Compton-Burnett (1884) was terrified of being alone. The quality she prized most in friends was – *availability*. So remember that if you have anyone born today. Her subtle, stilted 'conversation piece' style is an acquired taste.

6

Ninette de Valois (1898), founder of Sadlers Wells ballet, was a precocious 'miniature Pavlova'. Said she had danced on every pier in the country so the Dying Swan perhaps met the Silly Seagull of ebullient **Arthur Askey** (1900) in *his* early days. **Bjorn Borg** (1956) preferred to perform at Wimbledon.

7

'Beau' Brummel (1778), whose name still spells sartorial elegance, introduced starched neckcloths and glossier blacking. First man to wear black evening dress. A dry wit and cool impudence.
And as if that's not enough – a couple of Joneses to keep up with. Singer **Tom** (1940) and radio/TV presenter **Steve** (1945).

8

Composer **Robert Schumann** (1810) practised all day, flirted and argued all night and smoked incessantly. Crippled his hand with a DIY contraption intended to assist his playing. Abnormally sensitive and over-strung. Descending the musical scale here's **Nancy Sinatra** (1940), **Millicent Martin** (1934) and **Robert Preston** (1938), *The Music Man.*

9

Charles Saatchi (1943) director of the advertising firm which has the Conservative Party's account.
Cole Porter (1893), the ultimate in smart, sophisticated musical comedy, composer of evergreens like *Anything Goes.*
Writer **Nell Dunn** (1936) had an exotic childhood travelling with her brilliant mother. Contrariwise, longed for mum in frilly pinny!

10

Prince Philip (1920) and playwright **Terence Rattigan** (1911) both fit into the Gemini pigeonhole without much trimming off.
Robert Maxwell (1923) press tycoon.
Alan Randall ((1939) and fellow-Geminian George Formby sound-alike.
Judy Garland (1922) brilliant but brittle Geminian who tumbled off the tightrope.

11 Jackie Stewart (1939) racing driver.
Richard Strauss (1864), child prodigy, composed *Der Rosenkavalier*. His music was too modern for its day and produced riots, which were good news value.
Julia Margaret Cameron (1815) photographed all the eminent Victorians and was 'agitating company'. She 'ignored domesticity' and developed negatives all night.

12 Actor/author **Peter Jones** (1920). Royal couturière **Norman Hartnell** (1901).
Brigid Brophy (1929) intellectual, provocative novelist *(Hackenfellow's Ape)*. She and Maureen Duffy ran the Writers Action Group which pressurised Parliament into passing Authors' Public Lending Rights into law. Her astrological 'twin' is **Anne Frank** who wrote a famous diary . . .

13 **Dorothy Sayers** (1893), brilliant scholar and dualistic author of religious dramas and detective stories. Her Lord Peter Wimsey is a classic Gemini, all nerves and nose. Sherlock Holmes was somewhat similar and he was portrayed perfectly by **Basil Rathbone** (1892). Finally, keeping it clean for today – **Mrs Mary Whitehouse** (1910).

14 **Ché Guevara** (1928) Argentinian guerilla, and **Julie Ann Felix** (1938) folksinger, dominated student demos of the 60s and 70s but as a writer of propaganda for the underprivileged no one has yet touched **Harriet Beecher Stowe** (1811), author of *Uncle Tom's Cabin*.
Mike Yarwood (1941) could impersonate them all.

15 This *is* an astrology birthday book so 'musts' are the late **John Addey** of the Astrological Association (1920) and **Lieutenant Richard James Morrison RN** (1795) alias 'Zadkiel'. His cover was blown. The resultant publicity, although distasteful to Lieutenant Morrison, rocketted the circulation of *Zadkiel's Almanac*.
Richard Baker (1925), of course.

16 Two 'stirrers'. **Katherine Graham** (1917) owner and editor of *The Washington Post* Which sparked off Watergate, and **Enoch Powell MP** (1912). Gemini's keyword 'communication' acquires new meaning when Mr P. ascends the rostrum.
Authors **Victor Canning** (1911) and **Isabelle Holland** (1920) keep up the excitement.

17 **Ken Livingstone** (1945) leader of the GLC. Versatile actress **Beryl Reid** (1920) has married twice and gives her hobby as driving. Journalist **James Cameron** (1911). Singing stars **Dean Martin** (1917) and **Barry Manilow** (1946) who started off writing advertising jingles – a Geminian trade if ever!
The late **Sam Costa** (1910).

18 Unless one wishes to be torn apart by enraged Beatle fans **Paul McCartney** (1942) must take pride of place. At least, he's a home grown entertainer like **Ian Carmichael** (1920) who is well known for his interpretations of Lord Peter Wimsey and Bertie Wooster. From abroad: **Louis Jourdan** (1921) and **Jeanette Macdonald** (1906).

19 The **Duchess of Windsor** (1896), a cosmopolitan socialite. In the 1930s she was always in *Vogue* where she characterised that decade's ideal of pin-neat elegance. She paid meticulous attention to grooming and always looked as if she'd just been lacquered.
Elizabeth Seifert (1897), author of countless doctor/nurse romances.

20 **Catherine Cookson** (1906) has been called the most widely read author in England. A compulsive writer, has to sit up till all hours getting the story down. **Erroll Flynn** (1909) also wrote. *My Wicked, Wicked Ways* he called it. Actor, professional daredevil, fast driver, reckless adventurer, womaniser. Very rackety.

21 **Prince William** (1982) has the Sun in Cancer. It is usually still in Gemini today as it was for those two French left-wing intellectual cult figures, **Francoise Sagan** (1935) and **Jean-Paul Sartre** (1905).
But *we* exit dancing with **Enrico Cecchetti** (1850), greatest ever teacher of ballet!

NOTES

Cancer

22 June – 22 July

Cancerians are conditioned for ever by childhood experiences; they are hypersensitive, imaginative and retiring, swayed by the tides of the sea and influenced by the phases of the Moon, their ruling orb. They can be extremely moody in fact; they are sometimes crabbily bad-tempered yet at other times kind, considerate and sympathetic.

Running parallel with the strong but problematical link with mother is their attitude towards the home – they are tied to it but are great travellers too. Being basically insecure, the past and possessions mean a great deal to Cancerians and they hoard. In fact, they tend not to throw anything away – ever! – whether it's old letters (they're sentimental), baby bootees (they're maternal) or odd socks which might come in handy.

Of course, it's only sensible to have a little nest-egg put by for a rainy day. That's OK of course, but what they won't tell you is that the true Cancerian is prepared for a deluge! Many Cancerians do, in fact, amass fortunes; the rest would like to but are more inclined to spend their carefully hoarded 50ps on the family at Christmas.

Cancerians are good at handling money, other people's as well as their own, and can be quite shrewd in business matters. They have an eye for a bargain or a sound investment and an almost uncanny instinct for knowing what the public wants. They are the great providers of the zodiac; they also have tenacity and imagination so, whether nurses, caterers, publicans, sailors, explorers, dealers in antiques or real estate, gardeners, writers of historical novels or sentimental songs, should make enough to look after mum.

They are themselves wonderful parents, devoted to family and home life, they will always cherish their own loved ones. They are caring, sympathetic and understanding parents who have infinite patience and a genuine interest in their offspring; they are proud of their sons and protective towards their daughters. The only snag arises when the offspring start testing their wings preparatory to leaving the nest! Cancerians find it hard to believe that signs of independence in their loved ones don't indicate loss of affection.

This attitude pervades all their relationships and stems from an almost overwhelming feeling of insecurity. Emotional security is essential for Cancerian happiness. Ultra-sensitive and easily hurt, their inborn vulnerability means that they need constant reassurance and attention or will become moody and ill-tempered. Yet their sympathetic, warmly affectionate natures make Cancerians ideal marriage partners who will respond to understanding kindness with sincere devotion and enduring love.

Incurably romantic and deeply emotional, Cancerians may experience some difficulty in finding the right partner, however, due to their tendency to hide their own feelings and so making it very difficult to get to know them properly. Over-sensitive to criticism – real or imagined – they will retreat like the Crab back into their shells at the first sign of danger and not emerge again until long after the supposed trouble has passed!

Yet beneath that crabby exterior quivers a gentle Moon maiden . . . or knight in shining armour ready to provide protection.

Planetary Ruler   MOON
Element/Quality   WATER/CARDINAL
Keywords   DOMESTICITY, SENSITIVITY, IMAGINATION, MOODINESS
Day   MONDAY
Number   2
Colour   SILVER, PASTELS
Metal   SILVER
Stones   PEARLS, MOONSTONE, SELENITE, CHRYSOPRASE
Countries   HOLLAND, NEW ZEALAND, PARAGUAY, SCOTLAND
Places   In Britain: MANCHESTER, ROCHDALE, ST ANDREWS
  Elsewhere: ALGIERS, AMSTERDAM, BERN, GENOA, MILAN,
  STOCKHOLM, TUNIS, VENICE
Trees/Shrubs   WEEPING WILLOW, LIME, SYCAMORE
Flowers/Herbs   FLAX, CONVOLVULUS, LILIES, MELON VINE,
  SAXIFRAGE, PEAR BLOSSOM

22 As Cancer is the maternal sign **Esther Rantzen** (1940) makes a succulent starter. The arrivals and upbringings of Emily, Rebecca and Joshua were documented at length. And now today's triplets! 1910 produced romantic singer **Anne Ziegler** *(Only a Rose),* tenor **Peter Pears** *(Foggy, Foggy Dew)* and mountaineer **Lord Hunt** (Everest).

23 The **Duke of Windsor** (1894) fell for a succession of sophisticated, mature women, culminating with Mrs Simpson for whom he renounced all. In an earlier era it was Napoleon's fancy, **Josephine** (1763), who was the centre of dynastic storms. Up to date again with **Maggie Philbin** (1955) and **Adam Faith.**

24 **W. H. Smith** (1825), newspaper seller on a grand scale, went into politics and was made First Lord of the Admiralty. Immortalised by W.S. Gilbert in *HMS Pinafore* as Sir Joseph Porter, the Ruler of the Queen's Navee.
Coming Down Your Way, **Brian Johnston** (1912) and astronomer/author **Fred Hoyle** (1915).

25 This is the birthday of odd ode-man **Cyril Fletcher** (1913) and actor **Moray Watson** (1930). Both are keen gardeners. Still haunting his garden at Petworth is dear old **Fred Streeter** (1873) who nearly made his century. Today's birthday flower – not the flamboyant water lily but *his* favourite – the primrose.

26 Poet **Laurie Lee** (1914) author of *Cider With Rosie*. Let's hope those with birthdays today can wake up to a Laurie Lee morning – '. . . when love, Leans through geranium windows and calls with a cockerel's tongue' – and then have **June Bronhill** singing romantically in the orchard in the evening!

27 Starting with a laugh, 1938 'twins' – **Tommy Cannon,** comedian, and **Alan Coren,** entertainer and editor of *Punch*. Sobering up with **Helen Keller** (1880), US educator. Despite being deaf and blind from birth, she graduated from college, became a public figure, travelled widely and spoke up for the physically handicapped.

28 **Henry VIII** (1491 Old Style) had VI wives including Katherine the Arrogant, Anne of Cloves, Lady Jane Austen and Anne Hathaway. (See *1066 & All That,* although queried by Mastermind **Irene Thomas!).**
Juliet Dymoke (1919) traced her ancestry back to 1066 and was inspired to write historical novels.

29 Life began at forty for **Nicole, Duchess of Bedford** (1920). She fell in love with the Duke and felt, for the first time, that she was a *woman!* 'I have always felt 18. Age doesn't matter. It all comes from within.'
Appropriately, **Leroy Anderson** (1908) composed *Belle of the Ball.*

♋

30 The two faces of Cancer. **Lena Horne** (1917), the sultry, night-club beauty, who sang, memorably, *Stormy Weather,* and artist **Stanley Spencer** (1891) who stayed rooted in his native Cookham. When he painted *Christ Preaching* or *The Dead Rising,* it was always happening at Cookham – at the Regatta if possible.

1 A lot of lunar ladies: The **Princess of Wales** (1961) and her step-grandmother **Barbara Cartland** (1901), novelist **George Sand** (Baronne Dudevant) (1804) who knocked about with Chopin, actresses **Leslie Caron** (1931) and **Olivia de Havilland** (1916), airwoman **Amy Johnson** (1903), and one gentleman, TV presenter **Donny MacLeod** (1932).

2 Cancer is the sign of the Universal Provider, of knowing what the public wants, so **Lord Sieff** (1913), Chairman of Marks & Spencer, must come first. **Dr David Owen** (1938) of the SDP party is a keen Do-It-Yourselfer. True Crabs can make cosy homes from orange boxes.

3 Film director **Ken Russell** (1927) spent a lonely childhood staring out of the window but the Cancerian imagination exploded into films which had the critics convinced he was either a genius or had a mind like a sewer. A family man with five children. Popular novelist **Evelyn Anthony** (1928) has six.

4   **Dr Barnardo** (1845), father of seven, founded the Home for Destitute Children.
Gertrude Lawrence (1898) was the epitome of glamour – on the hotel balcony in *Private Lives* singing *Someday I'll Find You*, or arriving at the stage door in furs and orchids, escorted by a retinue of top-hatted young men.

5   **Cecil Rhodes** (1853), empire-building Crab, immensely rich and powerful, decreed that wider still and wider should his country's bounds be set and grabbed a chunk of Africa. They've got it back now.
Sarah Siddons (1755) alias Lady Macbeth and **Katherine Helmond** (1933) alias Jessica Tate in *Soap*.

6   **Sir Thomas Stamford Raffles** (1781), naturalist, initiator of the London Zoological Society and Government official in the Far East, founded Singapore.
Mignon Eberhart (1899) travelled widely and uses foreign locations for her mystery-romances.
Vladimir Ashkenazy (1937) practised and now plays the piano quite nicely – all over the world.

7   **Joseph Marie Jacquard** (1752), Lyons silk weaver. **Pierre Cardin** (1922), French fashion designer, introduced the first collection for men by a top designer, featuring bias cut and lavish colour. Leader in unisex wear.
A Goodie! **Bill Oddie** (1941).
A Beatle! **Ringo Starr** (1940).
A Unisex! **Dr Evadne Hinge.**

8 Not one **Rockefeller** but two! **John D.** (1839) and **Nelson** (1908) – a name synonymous with wealth. If you can't be rich, be cheerful with **Marty Feldman** (1933), or listen to the 'fripperies' of **Percy Grainger** (1882) – *Country Gardens* and *Molly on the Shore* are lovely titles for a summer's day.

9 Gothic horrors today! **Ann Radcliffe** (1764) wrote the famous *Mysteries of Udolpho*, **Matthew 'Monk' Lewis** (1773) *The Monk*, and **Mervyn Peake** (1911) the macabre *Gormenghast*.
Nikola Tesla (1856) is another mystery. The most brilliant engineer of all time – his electrical system runs the world today – he disappeared into oblivion.

10 **Marcel Proust** (1871) wrote *A la Recherché du Temps Perdu*, an evocation of childhood. He was intensely selfish yet so sensitive, so perceptive with regard to other people, that he charmed everyone. Another charmer, glamorous **Evelyn Laye** (1900) among the painted roses of **Redoute** (1759).
Whistler (1834) painted his mum.

11 'Softie' **Yul Brynner** (1915) 'wears a suit of armour in public life so he won't get hurt'. Singing twins for 1925: American soprano **Mattiwilda Dobbs** and Swedish tenor **Nicolai Gedda**. Soprano **Liza Lehmann** (1862) wrote the music to some quatrains from *Omar Khayyam* – *Myself When Young*, etc. Very successful.

12 Birthday of the mighty **Julius Caesar** (100 BC) after whom the month is named, and of the great Wagnerian singer **Kirsten Flagstad** (1895). Despite her heroic stage presence she was a very homely, placid woman.
And two more for 1895. Lyricist **Oscar Hammerstein II** *(The Sound of Music)* and architect **R. Buckminster Fuller.**

13 Lone yachtsman **Sir Alec Rose** (1908) sails past in *Lucky Lady.* Aboard are 6'5" reporter **Chris Serle** (1943); **Norman Tozer** (1934) with a birthday bargain or two; ex-professional rugby player and author **David Storey** (1933) whose 9th novel, *This Sporting Life,* was eventually accepted by the 15th publisher. Keep trying!

14 Ladies' Day. **Susan Howatch** (1940) writer of gothic romances and sprawling, complex family sagas covering several generations and told by different members of the family in turn – *Penmaric* and *Cashelmara.*
Gertrude Bell (1868), traveller, the 'uncrowned Queen of Arabia.'
Emmeline Pankhurst (1858), Suffragette leader.
Ruby Miller (1889), Gaiety Girl.

15 Writers: **Iris Murdoch** (1919), **Hammond Innes** (1913) and **Ann Jellicoe** (1927).
Lord Northcliffe (1865), pioneer newspaper proprietor. He sensed what the new semi-literate public wanted – short sentences, simple words, gossip and sensation. (And it still works!) Devoted to his mum. Achieved megalomania.
Guitarist **Julian Bream** (1933).

16 Camille Corot (1796) painted delicate, silvery, idyllic landscapes. (Silver and pastels are Cancer's colours.) A saintly and charitable bachelor, he would have been terrified of **Mrs Mary Baker Eddy** (1821) 'Mother' of the Christian Scientists, her dancing disciple **Ginger Rogers** (1911), **Mrs Mary Parkinson** (1939) and certainly **Lorraine Chase** (1951)!

17 James Cagney (1904), movie tough guy. 'A real softie at home' reported his wife of over 40 years.
Erle Stanley Gardner (1889), creater of Perry Mason, another Old Faithful.
John Astor (1763) amassed the family wealth from fur trading.
Over to you **Roy Galton** (1930) and **Tim Brooke-Taylor** (1940).

18 A cricketing birthday. Bulky, bearded **Dr W. G. Grace** (1848), the most famous man in England for 40 years. Not unknown at Lords are Australian **Dennis Lillee** (1949) and West Indian **Sir Garfield Sobers** (1936).
Joan (one of us) admires them all and, as Jean Merrill, writes *beautiful* romances!

19 Hubert Gregg (1914) of *Thanks for the Memory* and hoarder of old *Magnets* and *Gems*, says, 'I'm a Crab. I walk sideways and hide under rocks and keep myself to myself . . .'
Walking sideways too – actress **Beth Morris** (1949), actor **Simon Cadell** (1950), painter **John Bratby** (1928) and **Ilie Nastase** (1946).

20 Salvation Army Commissioner **Catherine Bramwell-Booth** (1883). Very religious but a tonic. Not so, Calvinist **Lord Reith** (1889), the BBC's first General Manager. He ruled with an iron rod and terrified everyone. Shy and aloof but worshipped his mother. Actress 'twins' for 1938, **Diana Rigg** and **Natalie Wood.**

21 *Mr & Mrs Hostess* **Susan Cuff** (1953), Miss Great Britain of 1975 and dress designer. **Dr Jonathan Miller** (1934) and 'twin' multi-millionaire property whizz kid **Nigel Broackes,** chairman of Trafalgar House. He loves travelling and is an accomplished goldsmith which shows we are getting near to Leo!

22 **Rose Kennedy** (1890), matriarch of the Kennedys, noted for her strength in face of crushing family tragedies.
Ernest Ball (1878) wrote many sentimental songs including *Mother Machree* and *When Irish Eyes Are Smiling.*
A romantic lunar fade-out with **Margaret Whiting** (1924) to sing *Moonlight in Vermont* (another Cancerian memory).

NOTES

Leo

23 July – 22 August

Known as the royal sign, Leo is ruled, appropriately enough, by the Sun and its subjects are seen at their best when actually born into the purple without any effort on their part, as so many of them are. To function properly, Leos need to be the centre of attraction and, happily, their magnetic personalities usually ensure that this is so.

Broad-minded, expansive and self-confident, they are also enthusiastic and most possess a keen sense of drama which, when combined with natural inspiration, gives them an unassailable aura of authority. Like the king of the beasts in the jungle, Leos are natural leaders who enjoy being boss; most are good organisers, too.

They love power and can cope with it, being able to delegate the boring or dirty jobs to lesser mortals without a twinge of guilt. These strong characters can, in fact, be quite bossy because they feel it is their birth-right to command true obedience, both in business matters and affairs of the heart.

These sunny, romantic, warm-hearted people attract the love and admiration of others easily. Their exceptional generosity of heart soon makes itself felt and Leos make friends quickly – sometimes too quickly because they are inclined to love and trust too readily; their willingness to believe the best of everyone can result in poor judgement.

Leos need mates whom they can look up to and admire – and who will respect and admire them in return. So they need to spend time getting to know their prospective partners well before making commitments. Then these magnanimous, passionate men and women should enjoy stimulating, rewarding and enduring relationships because they will express their feelings in a positive way, giving their hearts – and bodies – to their loved ones.

Very loyal to friends as well as lovers, Leos seem to have an in-built sense of honour; they won't let their side down whatever happens. In fact, they often do become involved in groups or organisations of one kind or another as they are good conversationalists and love to know everything that is going on around them. They will always be ready to get in their round, too, for Leos are very generous, in some cases extravagant with money.

But don't try to change a Leonian's mind if you are debating a point with him/her in a bar because, once Leos have made up their minds about something, that is it – they can at times be as stubborn as any Taurean. And it is definitely not a good idea to push them too far, either, because that loud, lionlike roar can be very embarrassing in public!

Not that Leos mind drawing attention to themselves, far from it. A desire to be in the limelight – quite literally – leads some of them to enter the acting profession or to become film producers. Others use their creative talents in different ways and become artists, jewellers or writers; Leos also make excellent teachers and children, of course, make appreciative audiences.

Remember, whether your own particular Lion or Lioness is dynamic, dazzling and dramatic or lazy, languid and luxury-loving, all Leos are members of the cat family so a little (or a lot!) of loving attention will quickly turn the most fiercesome roar into a purr!

Planetary Ruler   SUN
Element/Quality   FIRE/FIXED
Keywords   POWER, MAGNANIMITY, CREATIVITY, PRIDE
Day   SUNDAY
Number   1
Colour   ORANGE, WARM YELLOWS, GOLD
Metal   GOLD
Stones   AVENTURINE, GARNET, AMBER, DIAMOND
Countries   FRANCE, ITALY, RUMANIA, SYRIA
Places   In Britain: BATH, BLACKPOOL, BRISTOL, PORTSMOUTH,
  TAUNTON
  Elsewhere: BOMBAY, CHICAGO, CREMONA, DAMASCUS, PRAGUE,
  RAVENNA, PHILADELPHIA, ROME
Trees/Shrubs   LAUREL, WALNUT, JUNIPER, BAY, CITRUS, PALM
Flowers/Herbs   CELANDINE, MARIGOLD, PASSION FLOWER,
  ROSEMARY, RUE, SAFFRON, SUNFLOWER

♌

23 Your friends may still be Crabs, like historical novelist **Pamela Bennetts** (1903) but will probably want to be royal Lions like TV presenter **Michael Wood** (1948) – who did PhD research on medieval kingship! – and **Raymond Chandler** (1888), czar of hard-boiled crime writers, creator of private eye, Philip Marlowe.

24 **Alexandre Dumas** (1802), The *Lion* of Paris, wrote dramatic romances like *The Three Musketeers*. Childishly delighted with his success; bought palatial apartments and his own theatre. **Robert Graves** (1895), poet, wrote *I, Claudius* and *The White Goddess*. **John D. Macdonald** (1916) writes the Travis McGee thrillers, usually set in Florida.

25 All glittery rhinestones and showing off something rotten, pop star **Mick Jagger** (1942). From an earlier, more gracious stage, charming French actress **Yvonne Printemps** (1894), the star of Coward's *Conversation Piece*. More actors, **Cyril Luckham** (1907) and **William Marlowe** (1932).
All grist to the camera of **Vivienne** (1887), theatrical photographer.

26 **George Bernard Shaw** (1856), literary lion. Despite his awesome reputation he was in private a kind, friendly man. So was psychiatrist **Carl Jung** (1875) who coined the terms 'extraversion' and 'introversion' and gave credence to dream analysis.
Film makers **Blake** *(Pink Panther)* **Edwards** (1922) and **Stanley** *(2001)* **Kubrick** (1928).

27 **Robin Holmes a' Court** (1937) – there's an aristocratic Leonian name – actually one of the new Australian millionaires. He acquires problem companies (like Lord Grade's entertainment empire) and restores them to profitability. Collects vintage cars and paintings – a quiet man with expensive tastes.
Politicians **Shirley Williams** (1930) and **John Pardoe** (1934).

28 You'll have to shell out for diamonds today – if your friends include **Jackie Kennedy Onassis** (1929) that is!
Beatrix Potter (1866) was upper-class Kensington. She spent hours as a young woman in the Natural History Museum doing original research. For her nieces and nephews she drew animals which jumped off the page as Flopsy Bunnies, Peter Rabbit and Mrs Tiggywinkle.

29 **Arnold Weinstock** (1924), managing director of GEC.
Ruthless character, **Benito Mussolini** (1883). 'That he is a great man, I do not deny,' said Churchill, cautiously. A more attractive show-off than *Il Duce* was **Thelma Todd** (1905), pert, blonde, leading comedienne in many 2-reelers in the 1930s.

30 If a computer was doing this it would be singing in its nasty, electronic voice:
'Happy birthday **Clive Sinclair** [1940], Happy birthday to you.'
Sir Clive is Chairman of British Mensa and the developer of computers, calculators, digital watches, mini-TVs and *electric cars*. **Henry Ford** (1863) must be revolving!

♌

31

Princess Alexandra's daughter **Marina Ogilvy** (1966) appears for the British aristocracy, **Geraldine Chaplin** (1944), daughter of Sir Charles Chaplin, represents the United States, and her 'twin' **Jonathan Dimbleby** (1944), the dynastic Dimbleby family.
Economist **Milton Friedman** (1912) is *persona grata* at the White House and 10 Downing Street.

1

American **Herman Melville** (1819) wrote *Moby Dick*. He came of aristocratic stock and his father was an importer of French luxuries. **Yves St Laurent** (1936) *is* a French luxury, Crown Prince of the Dior fashion empire.
Lionel Bart (1930) won a gold disc for the sound track of *Oliver!*

2

Even the TUC has its hierarchy and at the top is **Len Murray** (1922). Other persons of note are **Alan Whicker** (1925), **Peter O'Toole** (1932) and **Myrna Loy** (1905).
John Tyndall (1820), Irish physicist, worked out why the sky is blue – and let's hope it is for today's birthday folk.

3

Terry Wogan (1938) will do the honours and usher in top crime writer **P. D. James** (1920) – the P stands for Phyllis – **Anthony Sampson** (1926) and 'twin' **Tony Bennett**; also the shades of poet **Rupert Brooke** (1887), the 'handsomest young man in England' and **Ernie Pyle** (1900), distinguished US war correspondent.

4 Queen Elizabeth, The Queen Mother (1900) scoops the royalty popularity stakes. Moving in the right circles, under the aegis of Maudie Littlehampton, is cartoonist **Osbert Lancaster** (1908) who has admitted to being a snob and a dandy!
Leonian poet **Percy Bysshe Shelley** (1792), 'the Sun-treader' as Browning called him.

5 Lions are members of the cat family. **Louis Wain** (1860) was the most popular cat artist ever. Known as 'the man who loved cats'. Does that fit in with your friends and relations born today? Otherwise there's **Neil Armstrong** (1930), the first Man in the Moon.

6 Some fizzing birthdays today! **Sir Freddie Laker** (1922), I-Love-**Lucille Ball** (1911) and her 'twin' the novelist **Constance Heaven.** Also **Barbara Windsor** (1936), **Moira Lister** (1923), mountaineer **Chris Bonnington** (1934), **Robert Mitchum** (1917), Campbell soup-tin artist **Andy Warhol** (1928) and – less fizzy! – poet-laureate **Alfred Lord Tennyson** (1809).

7 **'Alan Leo'** (1860), populariser of modern astrology, without whom . . .
Mata Hari (1876), exotic dancer, stripper, tart and unsuccessful spy. The French, of all people, shot her in 1917.
Dornford Yates (1885) wrote the hilarious *Berry* books, now black-listed for being beastly to foreigners. OK, let's substitute comedian **Duggie Brown** (1940).

♌

8

The perennial schoolboy birthday with a tuck-box celebration. Here's **Charles Hamilton** (1876) alias Frank Richards, creator of Greyfriars and Billy Bunter, and **F. Anstey** (1856) who wrote *Vice-Versa* where father was sent back to school. **Dustin Hoffman** (1937) starred in *Midnight Cowboy,* probably more to today's taste.

9

Tove Jansson (1914) had a happy Norwegian childhood and created the lovable Moomin family. She wouldn't be surprised to learn from Swiss child psychologist **Jean Piaget** (1896) that children think differently from adults! Neither would poet **Philip Larkin** (1922).
Dentist **William Morton** (1819) patented ether as an anaesthetic – bless him!

10

Harry Richman (1895), highly paid entertainer of the '30s with his elegant rendition of *Puttin' on the Ritz.* Even his name is Leonian! Magnificently gowned **Norma Shearer** (1900) was concurrently Queen of Hollywood.
In the 70s, topping the bill was **Ian Anderson** (1947) leader of the Jethro Tull rock group.

11

Noddy's birthday! **Enid Blyton** (1897) was the most popular children's author ever. Before her, **Charlotte May Yonge** (1823). For older readers, **William Haggard** (1907), **Angus Wilson** (1913) and **Alex Hailey** (1921).
Carrie Jacobs Bond (1862) wrote *When You Come To The End Of A Perfect Day –* hopefully, an appropriate sentiment.

12 George IV (1762), formerly Prince Regent, was fat and florid and had to be centre of attention. A generous patron of the arts, Brighton Pavilion, Regent Street, Regent's Park, are all 'Prinny's'.
Cecil B. de Mille (1881) founded Hollywood, perfected the bacchanalian orgy scene and expected to be treated like God.

13 Bert Lahr (1895) was the Cowardly Lion in the *Wizard of Oz*. Today's other Lions are, or were, in good roaring order: Fidel Castro of Cuba (1926), Sir Alfred Hitchcock (1899), Annie Oakley (1860), blind jazz pianist George Shearing (1919), comedian Bernard Manning (1930) and Rod Hull (1935) and Emu.

14 John Galsworthy (1867), creator of the gilded Forsytes and their Saga, was born with a silver spoon in his mouth. Albert Ball VC (1896), England's boy hero. Daredevil pilot in World War I, 'As straightforward and honest as he was fearless,' was killed in 1917 and buried with full military honours by the Germans.

15 Possibly the birthday of Sir Walter Scott (1771), Lawrence of Arabia (1888) and Napoleon (1769). Otherwise, Princess Anne (1950), actress Jenny Hanley (1947), choreographer John Cranko (1927), pianist Oscar Peterson (1925) and his 'twin' athlete/actor Mike Connors. More 'twins' – for 1912 – actress Wendy Hiller and good cook Julia Childs.

16 The novels of **Georgette Heyer** (1902) are set in the Regency period in the presence of that august Leonian, the Regent himself. She married a barrister but, un-Leo-like, never gave interviews. Not so actor **John Standing** (1939), actually Sir John Leon, 4th baronet, son of actress Kay Hammond.

17 The fabulous **Mae West** (1892) – Diamond Lil – lived in a fantasy world of plumed hats, hourglass moulded bodices and trailing skirts. She must have two male escorts at least so let's add 'Good Time' **George Melly** (1926), blues singer and balloon scriptwriter for *Flook,* and boxer **Alan Minter** (1951).

18 Almost royalty while Jimmy was President, **Rosalynn Carter** (1927). Other high-ranking Americans are, **Robert Redford** (1937), large, sexy **Shelley Winters** (1922) and **Marshall Field** (1834), founder of Chicago's No 1 store.
We have comedian and co-founder of *Private Eye,* **Willie Rushton** (1937), and even his hobby is 'going to America.'

19 As Louis XV's mistress, **Madame du Barry** (1743) virtually ruled France. Beautiful and lavish, she was guillotined, which is a fate some consider too good for **Richard Ingrams** (1937), editor of *Private Eye.*
Juvenile favourites, **E. Nesbit** (1858), author of *The Railway Children,* etc, and **Ogden Nash** (1902) – 'A little talcum is always walcum!'

20 Authors **Jacqueline Susann** (1921) and **H. P. Lovecraft** (1890). She was glamorous and her books were very sexy; *The Valley of the Dolls* was an all-time best seller. He was a gentleman and anglophile whose brand of horror fiction made him an international cult figure. 'Gentleman' **Jim Reeves** (1924).

21 Royals and aristocrats! **William IV** (1765), a bluff, amiable monarch; **Princess Margaret** (1930); **Count Basie** (1904), not actually a Count but one of the Jazz Kings; **Lord Goodman** (1913) the VIPs' solicitor and 'twin' **Sir Kenneth Cork,** their Receiver in bankruptcy; **Dame Janet Baker** (1933). Representing the plebs, **Barry Norman** (1933).

22 Composer **Claude Debussy** (1862) was indolent, aristocratic and feline, preferring cats (Siameses) to people. Leos do belong to the cat family. More members are **Honor Blackman,** snooker-playing **Steve Davis** (1957), humorist **Dorothy Parker** (1893) was a spit-kitten and sci-fi writer **Ray Bradbury** (1920) a witch's Grimalkin..

NOTES

Virgo

23 August - 22 September

Virgoans are ruled by Mercury and are, accordingly, clever and efficient, no detail escapes them. Virgo is one of the least complicated signs; its natives are realists who have few illusions about either life or people yet have an almost uncontrollable urge to sort out other people's lives, to make them as orderly and methodical as their own.

Unquestionably dependable and sincere, they make extremely capable nurses and doctors; many Virgoans do, in fact, enter the caring professions for Virgo is the sign of service to others. They tend to see life as a never ending series of tasks to be completed and, being worriers, worry endlessly about completing them: a trait that can lead to tension.

They can, though, become pernickety and obsessive for they are perfectionists (with a tendency to nag those of us who aren't!). Traditionally labelled as the sign of the hypochondriac, Virgo subjects are sometimes genuinely less than robust, so shouldn't be too hard on themselves. Physical fitness is admired, however, and some Virgoans do develop into dietary cranks.

Others put their analytical qualities to good use and become statisticians, research scientists, chemists or, indeed, detectives or literary critics, short-story writers, essayists or draughtsmen. Teaching is another profession that may appeal to the Virgoan character because they revere education; they also have a flair for figurework, so may become accountants.

Virgo is also the sign of the craftsman and many born under it enter trades or professions where their eye for detail and their manual dexterity can be usefully combined. But, whatever they decide to do for a living, and the choice is wide, they make excellent employees because they are loyal, industrious and thoroughly trustworthy – qualities that often result in material success.

They may never accumulate vast wealth, but will always budget carefully, are great bargain-hunters and usually invest any surplus from their hard-earned cash wisely. Prudent in all things, their modest demeanor is frequently mistaken for prudishness. Yet the fact that Virgoans are not the type to go in much for public displays of emotion does not mean that they haven't got any.

Beneath the mantle of practicality, order and analytical thinking lies a poetic, romantic soul, the kind of person reminiscent of Edwardian garden parties or Arthurian legends. Kind, gentle and sympathetic, Virgoans possess natural goodness of heart and give all of themselves to those in need or those they love. Although selective in their relationships, they are responsive, considerate spouses, conscientious parents and loyal friends.

Fastidious in all things, Virgoans are notoriously neat and tidy. Their homes, offices, cars and personal appearance are immaculate and, as they have discriminating taste as well as an eye for detail, they have earned a well-deserved reputation for elegance.

But, besides impeccable dress and manners, Virgoans have another talent which often goes unremarked. Shrewd, subtle, mentally agile and sharp, they are wonderfully entertaining conversationalists and superbly witty raconteurs for, like Geminians, they are children of Mercury!

Planetary Ruler   MERCURY
Element/Quality   EARTH/MUTABLE
Keywords   SERVICE, ORDERLINESS, SHREWDNESS, WIT
Day   WEDNESDAY
Number   5
Colour   SOFT BROWN & GREEN, DUSKY COLOURS
Metal   PLATINUM/ALUMINIUM
Stones   PINK JASPER, CHALCEDONY, AGATE, TOURMALINE
Countries   BRAZIL, CRETE, IRAQ, SWITZERLAND, TURKEY, URUGUAY, WEST INDIES
Places   In Britain: BURY, CHELTENHAM, MAIDSTONE, READING
   Elsewhere: BOSTON, JERUSALEM, LOS ANGELES, LYONS, STRASBOURG, TOULOUSE, PARIS
Trees/Shrubs   SILVER BIRCH, FILBERT, NUT BEARERS
Flowers/Herbs   ANEMONE, BLUE MORNING GLORY, CARAWAY, STARWORT, WATER PLANTAIN

♍

23 Those born today might be Leo or Virgo. Composer **Constant Lambert** (1905) is a good link. His ballet *Horoscope* concerns a Sun-Leo who loves a Sun-Virgo. As part Leo himself he had a dominating physical presence and personality; as part Virgo, one became his friend by invitation only.

24 Journalist **Maurice Richardson** (1907), specialist in mini-reviews of thrillers, guaranteed to grip 'like Princess Anne's knees' or 'Pierrepoint's farewell handshake'. **Max Beerbohm** (1872), the 'incomparable Max,' wit, critic and exquisite essayist, said, 'My gifts are small – I've used them well and discreetly.' A Lilliputian birthday, disregarding organist **Carlo Curley** (1952)!

25 **Sean Connery** (1930) has Virgo's physical fitness fetish and he'll always be the secret service agent, James Bond, to most of us. Founder of the US secret service was martinet **Allan Pinkerton** (1819) of Pinkerton's Detective Agency. **Leonard Bernstein** (1918) composed *West Side Story*. **Dorothy Dunnett/Dorothy Halliday** (1923) writes historical novels and thrillers.

26 Only Virgo could produce such a paragon as Victoria's Consort, **Prince Albert** (1819). He was good, he was clever, he was handsome, he was faultless. Early and late he was at his desk arranging, drafting, corresponding, writing endless tidy memoranda and organising – brilliantly – the profit-making Great Exhibition of 1851.

27 Lloyd C. Douglas (1877) wrote *The Robe*, depicting the self-enrichment which results from serving others. **Mother Teresa** (1910) is a living embodiment of this.
In addition, actress **Tuesday Weld** (1943) and authors **Antonia Fraser** (1932), **Norah Lofts** (1904), **C. S. Forester** (1899) of *Captain Hornblower* fame and **Ira Levin** (1929) of *Rosemary's Baby*.

28 Sombre birthday thought from German poet **Goethe** (1749) – 'A useless life is an early death' – so, take stock!
Unassuming Poet Laureate **John Betjeman** (1906) has always shown a passionate interest in Victorian churches and is the poet of the suburbs, where Joan Hunter-Dunn played endless tennis.

29 Your greetings card may very well be a Hallmark (advert). The firm's founder, **Joyce Clyde Hall,** was born today in 1891. Also looking at the back to see, will be **Lady Diana Duff Cooper, Viscountess Norwich** (1892), **Dinah Washington** (1924), **Richard Attenborough** (1923), **Elliott Gould** (1938) and **Lenny Henry** (1958).

30 Politician: **Denis Healey** MP (1917). Biographer: **Lady Longford** (1906). Actresses: **Shirley Booth** (1907), **Joan Blondell** (1909), **Deborah Kerr** (1921), **Elizabeth Ashley** (1941). Singer: **Dana** (1951). Skier: **Jean Claude Killy** (1943) and 'twin'; cartoonist: **R. Crumb.** Railwayman: **Sir Peter Parker** (1924). Writer and interviewer: **John Gunter** (1901). Who have you got?

31 **Maria Montessori** (1870) worked in a children's psychiatric clinic and devised the famous Montessori teaching system. But it's not all work and no play. Here are comedians **Roy Castle** (1932) and **Larry Grayson** (1930), also lyricist/playwright **Alan Jay Lerner** (1918) of *My Fair Lady, Camelot*, etc.

1 Fisticuffs with **'Gentleman' Jim Corbett** (1866) and **Rocky Marciano** (1923) both of whom could have been floored by Tarzan of the Apes who is entered in the lists by **Edgar Rice Burroughs** (1875).
A birthday drink with Ena Sharples – sorry, **Violet Carson** (1905) and **Barry Gibb** of the Bee Gees (1946).

2 Anyone for tennis? Here's **Jimmy Connors** (1952). Cowering behind the net are actors **Derek Fowlds** (1937), **Francis Matthews**/Paul Temple (1931); authors and journalists **Mike Lloyd Williams** (1943), **Glyn Worsnip** (1938), **Allen Drury** (1918); dancer **Marge Champion** (1923); and jazzman **Horace Silver** (1928) *Blowin' the Blues Away!*

3 Murdering Virgos go for poison. American **Florence Maybrick** (1862) married an elderly Liverpudlian – who died. In Mr Maybrick's stomach were found arsenic, prussic acid, strychnine, morphine and hyoscine. Lancastrians take some polishing off. Mrs M. got 15 years but, being a literary Virgo, wrote a book on the experience.

4 Band-leader **Geoff Love** started work as a motor mechanic. **Henry Ford II** (1917) started as director and vice-president of the family automobile firm. A workaholic, all his efficient ruthlessness was needed to ditch old Henry and revitalise the company.
Writers **Joan Aiken** (1924) and **Mary Renault** (1905), a former nurse.

5 A few birthday mates **Russell Harty** (1934) *hasn't* met! **James 'Cunning' Murrell** (1780) Essex herbalist, wart charmer and dowser; composer **Giacomo Meyerbeer** (1791); desperado **Jesse James** (1847).
We can't answer for **Raquel Welch** (1940); comedian **Bob Newhart** (1929); writers **Frank Yerby** (1916) and **Arthur Koestler** (1905); couturière **Edward Molyneux** (1894).

6 Some earnest gents born today. **Sir Edward Appleton** (1892) discovered the ionosphere; **John Dalton** (1766) evolved an atomic theory; aloof, reserved **Montague Norman** (1871) joined the Bank of England as a part-timer and was its Governor a few years later. **Bernie Winters** . . . well, Bernie Winters was born in 1932.

7 **Buddy Holly** (1936) was a major influence in early rock 'n' roll. **Grandma Moses** (1860) was better known for her 'primitive' paintings of US rural life.
Edith Sitwell (1887), poet, was recognised everywhere for her distinctive Plantagenet looks, and **Group Captain Leonard Cheshire** VC (1917) for founding the Cheshire Homes for the chronically ill.

8 Two Goons! **Peter Sellers** (1925) and spherical **Harry Secombe** (1921). Harry Secombe also writes and works hard for charity, while Peter Sellers radiated executive-type tension and said that without the greasepaint he had no personality – so perhaps Virgo does play some part after all.

9 The 9th day of the 9th month – *Luck!* **Countess Spencer** (1929), stepmother to Princess Diana, has shot up in Debrett. (9-9-9 – no wonder). Such a fusspot that her mother (Barbara Cartland) feared she would be an old maid.
Another 9-9-9-er, **Beverley Nichols** (1899), who was a delightful author and gardener.

10 Critic **Cyril Connolly** (1903) wrote, 'astrologers find this love of perfection in those born under Virgo.' His own output was limited but exquisite. Other perfectionists: golfer **Arnold Palmer** (1929), dancer **Adèle Astaire** (1897), shocking-pink couturière **Elsa Schiaparelli** (1896) and **Fay Wray** (1907) who screamed beautifully in *King Kong!*

11 **Erastus Beadle** (1821) popularised the dime novel, forerunner of today's paperback, and deserves thanks from all authors, including: **William Golding** (1911) *Lord of the Flies,* **D. H. Lawrence** (1885) *Lady Chatterley's Lover,* **Sir James Jeans** (1877) *The Mysterious Universe,* **Jessica Mitford** (1917) *The American Way of Death,* and short story writer **O. Henry** (1862).

12 Surprisingly, the city of Paris comes under Virgo and who more Parisian than **Maurice Chevalier** (1888) and his 'twin' **Louis Icart** who painted naughty nudes with great success in the '20s and '30s. Virgo has its moments! It also has **Linda Gray** (1941) otherwise Sue-Ellen of *Dallas*. She was a top fashion model.

13 **Claudette Colbert** (1905) is 'her clever, witty, typically Parisian self,' wrote film critic James Agee. So fastidious she washed her gold bracelets every day. Properly awestruck are **Jacqueline Bissett** (1946), singer **Mel Tormé** (1925) and **J. B. Priestley** (1894), author of *The Good Companions* and almost a literary monolith.

14 **Sir Peter Scott** (1909), artist, writer, ornithologist, founder of World Wildlife Fund and tireless worker for conservation. The **Hon Angus Ogilvy** (1928), Princess Alexandra's husband, is Patron of the Scottish Wildlife Trust.
If only **Mr Gillie Potter** (1887), Hogsnorton's most famous son, could still be 'speaking to us in English'!

15 **Agatha Christie** (1890). Her Hercule Poirot, so neat, fastidious and clever, and moralising, old-maidy Miss Marple, are perfect representations of Virgo.
Richard Gordon (1921) wrote the *Doctor* books – a subject dear to Virgo's heart.
Soprano **Hilda Guedon** (1917). Her voice is cool, crystal clear and nearly impeccable. That's Virgo too!

16 **Anna Kingsford** (1846) purchased and edited *The Lady's Own Paper* and used it as a platform to oppose vivisection and to promote higher education for women. Studied medicine in Paris, became a vegetarian, wrote *The Perfect Way in Diet*, and was strikingly beautiful; so too is actress **Lauren Bacall** (1924).

17 **John Creasey** (1908) wrote 560 thrillers in 40 years. *The Toff, The Baron, Dr Palfrey, Gideon of the Yard, Inspector West.* Had a card index system, a production line of work in progress and 28 pseudonyms. Died of overwork. Another author, just as thrilling but more romantic, **Mary Stewart** (1916).

18 **Greta Garbo** (1905), the nonpareil of beauty for any sign. Reclusive and remote. 'Co-starring with Garbo hardly constituted an introduction' declared Frederic March. Crashing back to earth and into the kitchen – trust a Virgo to have manufactured the first washing machine! It was **Elmer Henry Maytag** (1883).

19 **Arthur Rackham** (1867). His paintings are eerie and haunting with spectral trees and spidery witches. **Twiggy** (1949) had a distinctly Arthur Rackham look about her when modelling. In 1977 was voted the World's Loveliest Woman. Person she would most like to meet – Greta Garbo.
Fashion designer **Zandra Rhodes** (1940).

20 Actress **Sophia Loren** (1934) lives simply and in seclusion. 'I only spend my time doing things I consider worthwhile . . . Work is everything to me, though I sometimes think I would like to write.' Who doesn't? Actor **Kenneth More** (1914) wrote *Happy-Go-Lucky*, musician **John Dankworth** (1927) – well, nothing yet, except music, of course.

21 Superwoman: **Shirley Conran** (1932). Superman: **Ian MacGregor** (1912), brought over to do something about British Steel and then British Coal. Famous Author: **H. G. Wells** (1866). Composer and astrologer: **Gustav Holst** (1874) who wrote *The Planets* including, of course, Mercury. Finally **Jimmy Young** and J. R. himself, **Larry Hagman** (1931).

22 Changing signs. Virgo to Libra. Novelist **Rosamunde Pilcher** (1924) tries to 'strike a balance' (Libra). Writes for intelligent women (Virgo) who sometimes want to read a romantic novel (Libra). The Americans have taken her up – lucky girl.
Michael Faraday (1791), pioneer in the development of electricity and very nice man.

NOTES

Libra

23 September - 22 October

Libra is ruled by Venus, planet of love and beauty. Its symbol is the scales or the Balance, the only inanimate object in the zodiac, and many Librans are themselves like the scales, they sway from one emotional extreme to the other for Libra is a dualistic sign.

Sometimes known as lazy Libra, this description is not really fair, it's just that these people are so busy weighing up the pros and cons of every situation that they give the false impression of doing little or nothing a good part of the time. But the accusation of indecisiveness does have more credence!

Librans can be temperamentally very inconsistent – one minute good-natured, friendly folk, stubborn and argumentative the next. Other signs may find this confusing; don't worry, so do Librans. It all boils down to the fact that Librans have a habit of trying to be all things to all men in their efforts to keep everyone happy, everything on an even keel . . . to maintain a balance, in fact.

But, once they have made up their minds, Librans can be surprisingly dogged about getting their own way for a sign with the reputation of pliability. Of course, they may try to get what they want by exercising charm, persuasion and tact, but if this doesn't work they will use cold logic, scathing sarcasm, guile and can be as tough as old boots if the soft sell fails.

They will, though, always try the soft option first because Librans don't like disharmony or discord: it can make them physically ill. Sociable, with a sunny, agreeable manner, and an infectious smile, they thrive on companionship and become depressed if on their own for long periods, although they do need some privacy and will respect that of others.

Librans have natural tact and diplomacy and make splendid middlemen of any sort so may become diplomats, negotiators, arbiters or mediators; the legal profession also holds obvious attractions for those born under the sign of the Balance, as does social or welfare work. They dislike dirty or unpleasant working conditions and need to work in congenial surroundings, preferably with others.

Most Librans have artistic or creative abilities and many of them enter the luxury or beauty trades or become designers, artists, draughtsmen, architects and so on. Others take up occupations concerned with musical or theatrical entertainment, perhaps as directors or managers for they usually have good administrative ability and keen business sense.

Libra is the sign of partnership and its subjects function much better with a partner than on their own, in business and personal life. Of course, it may not always be the same partner because they do tend to rush into relationships in their eagerness to share their lives. They are also very idealistic so will be deeply hurt if their idols prove to have feet of clay.

Yet they are not willing to suffer discord and would far rather end an association that has gone awry than continue with it. Basically, though, Librans long for love and marriage – the two being almost inseparable to the Libran mind – and will actively seek them all their lives if necessary, even if the search is conducted with such subtlety and charm that the quarry is unaware of being hunted by these romantic, intuitive, intelligent manipulators!

Planetary Ruler VENUS
Element/Quality AIR/CARDINAL
Keywords JUSTICE, HARMONY, DIPLOMACY, PARTNERSHIP
Day FRIDAY
Number 6
Colour PALE GREEN, PINK, BLUE
Metal COPPER
Stones SAPPHIRE, ROSE QUARTZ, LABRADORITE, OPAL
Countries AUSTRIA, BURMA, CHINA, ARGENTINA, JAPAN, TIBET
Places In Britain: LEEDS, NOTTINGHAM
   Elsewhere: ANTWERP, CHARLESTON, COPENHAGEN, LISBON, FRANKFURT, VIENNA, JOHANNESBURG, FRIBOURG
Trees/Shrubs PEACH, PEAR, BOX, SYCAMORE
Flowers/Herbs CLOVE, COLUMBINE, FIGWORT, PRIMULA, VIOLET

23

Delightful **Jane Taylor** (1783) wrote nursery rhymes like *Twinkle, Twinkle, Little Star* and *I Love Little Pussy*. Modern **Romy Schneider** (1938) acted in *What's New Pussycat?* Blind jazz singer and composer, **Ray Charles** (1930). Romantic novelist **Baroness Orczy** (1865) wrote *The Scarlet Pimpernel*.

24

A. P. Herbert (1890) studied law, went into Parliament and wrote about everything including Ms Libra herself! (Well, that's what it sounds like.) 'Not huffy or stuffy, not tiny or tall; But fluffy, just fluffy, with no brains at all!' Certainly not descriptive of Mrs Paul McCartney – **Linda** – a professional photographer.

25

Ronnie Barker (1929) has an eye for a pretty girl, so had **C. B. Cochrane** (1872). Mr Cochrane's Young Ladies were famous on the revue stage in shows like *One Damned Thing After Another*. Of tougher metal no doubt, highly-paid **Barbara Walters** (1931), US TV anchorwoman.

26

Edith Holden, the Edwardian Lady whose artistic diary for the year 1906 swept the country, was born today in 1871.
Another well-known female is singer **Olivia Newton-John** (1948).
For the gentleman, poet **T. S. Eliot** (1888), and **George Gershwin** (1898) whose *Rhapsody in Blue* shall be the birthday treat.

27 **Rosa Lewis** (1867), the Duchess of Duke Street, probably celebrated her birthdays with Edwardian spreads at the Cavendish. Guests of honour: **Vincent Youmans** (1898) composer of *No, No, Nanette* and **Sir Bernard Miles** (1907) of the Mermaid Theatre. If an aspirin is needed, thank the chemist **Adolph Kolbe** (1818).

28 Lovely **Brigitte Bardot** (1934) escorted by actor **Peter Finch** (1916) and **Sapper** (1888), author of the Bulldog Drummond books which are fast becoming popular again. He was an officer (a Colonel with the Royal Engineers) and a gentleman. In the swimming pool, *Not Waving, But Drowning!* – poet **Stevie Smith** (1902).

29 **Francois Boucher** (1703) painted a once-upon-a time world of frills and lace, plunging necklines and Cinderella slippers. Pretty, cultured **Mrs Gaskell** (1810) painted a lavender-scented world in *Cranford*. Her books have been described as 'gleaming, delicate little bits of lustre pottery, as fresh as this morning's roses.'

30 Libran entertainers born today include: **Jack Wild** (1952), **Rula Lenska** (1947), **Ian Ogilvie** (1943), **Johnny Matthis** (1935), **Angie Dickinson** (1931), **Donald Swann** (1923), **Deborah Kerr** (1921), **David Oistrakh** (1908) and **Frank Lawton** (1904) – and many, many more.
For a good read there's **Michael Innes** (1906) and **Truman Capote** (1924).

1

One of us (**Jo**) a maker of talismans in precious metals, wants to be remembered today along with **Julie Andrews** (1934) working with whom is 'like being hit over the head with a Valentine,' **Stanley Holloway** (1890), reporter **Sandy Gall** (1927) and ex-President **Jimmy Carter** (1924).

2

The Archbishop of Canterbury **Dr Runcie** (1921). The militant pacifist **Gandhi** (1869). Author **Graham Greene** (1904), whose novels contain a strong religious dimension. For the media-conscious – TV presenters **Anna Ford** (1943) and **Roz Hanby** (1951), the latter was a stewardess with British Airways who chose her as their poster girl.

3

Jazz aficionados born today will welcome the company of **Art Tatum** (1910) and **Chubby Checker** (1941) who popularised the Twist dance craze. For the others – actor **Michael Hordern** (1911) and **Johnny Burke** (1908) who wrote popular songs like *Pennies from Heaven. So, if it's raining, have no regrets.* . .

4

Designer **Sir Terence Conran** (1931) went into shopkeeping to sell his own goods and launched Habitat. He wanted cheerfulness, colour and light not a 'sea of brown squares.' **Damon Runyon** (1880), an habitué of Broadway, would have approved. He wrote the book of the musical *Guys & Dolls.*

5
Showbiz twins for 1923 – **Barbara Kelly** and **Glynis Johns.** The latter has a 'molasses and honey voice.' The song, *Send in the Clowns* was written for her. **Barbara Kelly** married Bernard Braden when she was 17. She was the ambitious one and pushed him here all the way from Canada!

6
Le Corbusier (1887), Swiss city planner, revolutionised architecture with *La Ville Radieuse* which he designed in 1930. 'The essential joys are sun, space and verdure' he decreed and his 'twin', the beautiful opera singer **Maria Jeritza** called her autobiography *Sunlight & Song.*
Actresses **Britt Ekland** (1942) and **Carole Lombard** (1908).

7
Birthday sentiment from **James Whitcomb Riley** (1849), author of *Little Orphan Annie:*
For the world is full of roses, and the roses full of dew,
And the dew is full of heavenly love that drips fer me and you
Mellow-voiced **Al Martino** (1927) would make it sound good anyway!

8
Great Scott, it's Maynard! Actor **Bill Maynard** (1928) whose Libran hobby is watching other people work, and snooker. Right, professional snooker player coming up – **Ray Reardon** (1932).
Author **Frank Herbert** (1920) best known for his sci-fi *Dune* books.
Artist **Sir Alfred Munnings** (1878).
Ballerina **Merle Park** (1937).

9

The rival runners Sebastian Coe (29 September 1956) and **Steve Ovett** (today 1955) are both Librans. Libra works best with an opposite number as a balance or spur. **John Lennon** (1940) had the Beatles and, of course, Yoko.
Lord Hailsham (1907), as Lord Chancellor, holds the Scales of Justice anyway.

10

Jean Watteau (1684) painted gallants and ladies in silks and satins romancing in idealised sylvan settings.
In the wings are **Judith Chalmers, Martina Navratilova** (1956), romantic novelist **Sheila Walsh** (1928) and 'twin' **Nicholas Parsons.** 35-stone wrestler **Giant Haystacks** (1947) somehow seems out of place!

11

Lots of Libran ladies become celebrities under their husbands' names. Today there's **Eleanor Roosevelt** (1884), wife of Franklin D., herself a popular columnist and broadcaster, and our own **Anne Purvis** (1952), weather forecaster, wife of George. Famous under the name of Revlon is **Charles Revson** (1906), world's largest cosmetics manufacturer.

12

Aleister Crowley (1875), the 'wickedest man in the world,' had a first-class brain and great charm. His (distorted) Libran Law was 'do as thou wilt.' Practised black magic and was said to have raised the Devil. A dubious birthmate for **Angela Rippon** (1944), **Magnus Magnusson** (1929), **Luciano Pavarotti** (1935).

13 **Mrs Lily Langtry** (1852). The Jersey Lily was tall and curvacious with violet eyes, peachbloom complexion and masses of Titian hair. 'To look at Lily is to imagine one is dreaming' (Whistler).
Mrs Margaret Thatcher (1925) has been described as a 'cold-water English Rose.' A flowery sort of day.

14 *I Like Ike* was the presidential election slogan of **Dwight Eisenhower** (1890) and everybody did. They all like **Cliff Richard** (1940) too. *And* actress **Lilian Gish** (1896) – 'an expensive doll made of the best quality porcelain with teeth of seed pearls and hair spun from a spider's web' (Beaton).

15 Birthday thought: 'One should never trust a woman who tells one her real age. A woman who would tell one that would tell one anything' – **Oscar Wilde** (1854).
P. G. Wodehouse (1881) wrote for pleasure, no message for humanity, no brooding over the cosmos; just one of the butterflies which loafed about Blandings!

16 **Max Bygraves** (1922), **Peter Bowles** (1936) and **Angela Lansbury** (1925) get the party swinging.
Birthday celebrities to be remembered are **Kathleen Winsor** (1919) who wrote *Forever Amber,* actress **Linda Darnell** (1921) who starred in it, and the **Earl of Cardigan** (1797) who led the Charge of the Light Brigade, and invented the woolly.

17 Today's beauties include **Elinor Glyn** (1864) who invented *It*. She had auburn hair and green eyes and her book *Three Weeks* disgusted everyone who read it – and everyone did. In her heyday, red-haired **Rita Hayworth** (1918) was billed as the 'Love Goddess'. For today's thrills, **Evel Knievel** (1938) stunt motor-cyclist.

18 **Pierre Trudeau** (1919) Canadian Prime Minister, playboy and pacifist. Not so pacific, Greek actress **Melina Mercouri** (1925) – *Never on Sunday* – who fought the ruling military junta and, on its fall, was elected to Parliament and made Minister of Culture and Sciences. Currently engaged in a campaign to get back the Elgin Marbles from us.

19 **John Le Carré** (1931) was a diplomat – Libran occupation – before becoming writer of spy stories, such as *The Spy Who Came In From The Cold, Tinker, Tailor, Soldier Spy* and *Smiley's People*, which present new perspectives on espionage and ask if evil can only be met with evil.
Nice Canadian actor **Robert Beatty** (1909).

20 **Viscount Palmerston** (1784) did very well at the War Office, his invariable reaction to trouble being to send a gunboat. Popular with the people and a favourite with the ladies. Disraeli called him a painted pantaloon (he dyed his whiskers!). At 55 he married a widow of 52 – result, happiness.

21 Samuel Taylor Coleridge (1772), poet. *The Ancient Mariner, Christabel* and *Kubla Khan* are spellbinding fantasies. Coleridge bewitched everyone. Charles Lamb called him 'an Archangel, slightly damaged.'
Also in the fantasy business **Ursula le Guin** (1929). Her science fiction wins regular awards. (Thought: **Alfred Nobel** was born today in 1833!)

22 Reading **E. Phillips Oppenheim** (1866) we are translated to a world of millionaires, mysterious, bejewelled women, the Riviera, luxury yachts, gambling at Monte – in company perhaps with **Dory Previn** (1925), **Joan Fontaine** (1917), **Catherine Deneuve** (1943) and the ghost of **Franz Liszt** (1811), Hungarian composer/pianist, the man mobbed by princesses.

NOTES

Scorpio

23 October – 21 November

Pluto, the planet named after the god of the underworld, has rulership over the sign of Scorpio although it was attributed to Mars before the discovery of this planet. Scorpios are dominated by powerful emotions and, whatever their activities, have a sense of purpose and the determination to see things through to the bitter end if necessary.

Scorpio is the sign most closely associated with the fundamentals of life – sex, birth and death – and its subjects are usually spectacular in all departments! They take life seriously and are the most passionate and intense of all the signs of the zodiac. They never do anything by halves; they are definitely, absolutely either this or that.

Most Scorpios have great personal magnetism which others find intriguing for there is something fascinating, dynamic and exciting about them. They do, however, sometimes have difficulty understanding their own reactions to problems or situations, so can be their own worst enemies. There is probably a greater range of temperament within the Scorpio character than in any other sign.

They are often followers of lost causes and will go to the stake for their beliefs. Some have mystical revelations and follow religious or occult paths; others turn their passion for secrecy and intrigue in other directions and enter politics. Medicine and social work are favoured occupations, too, as are the law, the police and the armed forces.

But, whatever they do, Scorpios are competitive and fiercely ambitious because they like to prove to themselves and others that they can do everything a little better than the next person. They find such battles stimulating for they have boundless mental energy and an indestructible spirit.

Industrious and purposeful, Scorpios will nearly always achieve what they set out to do because they are quite prepared to persevere indefinitely. Even when a venture seems destined for failure, resourceful Scorpios will find a way to turn a potentially hazardous situation to advantage; they have hidden depths and often succeed where others would fail.

They have hidden depths when it comes to romance too. Often known as the sexiest sign of the zodiac, Scorpios can love or hate with equal fervour. They make bad enemies but good friends, for they will express themselves candidly and will never forget an injury nor a favour.

Passionate, ardent and strong-willed, they take their relationships seriously and long to possess the one they love . . . and there's the nub of the problem. Scorpios are wildly jealous and madly possessive of their loved ones, or even their prospective loved ones, come to that!

Yet, if they can curb this particular trait, Scorpios have every chance of finding what they want from life and, what is more, keeping it. They have forceful personalities and it is difficult for others to resist their mysterious allure, their magnetism and sexuality for they understand the hidden longings of others – and can fulfil these.

SCORPIO

Planetary Ruler   PLUTO
Element/Quality   WATER/FIXED
Keywords   REGENERATION, INTENSITY, SECRECY, PASSION
Day   TUESDAY
Number   9
Colour   DARK RED, BROWN, BLACK
Metal   IRON, STEEL
Stones   MALACHITE, OBSIDIAN, SMOKE QUARTZ, JASPER
Countries   ALGERIA, BAVARIA, MOROCCO, NORWAY, TRANSVAAL
Places   In Britain: DOVER, HALIFAX, HULL, LIVERPOOL,
   NEWCASTLE-UPON-TYNE, STOCKPORT, WORTHING
   Elsewhere: BALTIMORE, CINCINNATI, GHENT, MILWAUKEE,
   NEW ORLEANS, WASHINGTON D.C.
Trees/Shrubs   REDWOODS, BLACKTHORN, ELM, MAHOGANY
Flowers/Herbs   BAMBOO, DEADLY NIGHTSHADE, LILAC, MUSTARD,
   BRONZE CHRYSANTHEMUM

OCTOBER

23 Those born today are still more likely to have the Sun in Libra rather than Scorpio but one expects to find traces of Scorpio at least. Definitely Librans are novelist **Jean Stubbs** (1926) and actress **Diana Dors** (1931).
Uncertain are 1940 'twins' – cricketer **Geoffrey Boycott** and Brazilian footballer **Pelé**.

24 Operatic star **Tito Gobbi** (1915) studied the character he was portraying in depth even making a plastic model of it and compiling a dossier of psychological and physiological traits. Thriller writer **Ted Allbeury** (1917) probably does the same.
Robin Day (1923) probes.
On the other side, the **Kray Twins** (1933).

25 Mastermind **Fred Housego** (1944) would undoubtedly know all about his birthday mates, i.e. **Pablo Picasso** (1881); **Georges Bizet** (1838) composer of *Carmen;* the great **Lord Macaulay** (1800); **Rear-Admiral Richard Byrd** (1888), American aviator and polar explorer; and **Johann Strauss** the Younger (1825), the one who wrote *The Blue Danube.*

26 Choose today between a sonata on the harpsichord from **Domenico Scarlatti** (1685) or **Mahalia Jackson** (1911), gospel singer, belting out *Onward, Christian Soldiers.* Also present, TV presenter **Shaw Taylor** (1924) and TUC leader **Hugh Scanlon** (1913). This was the birthday of the late **Shah of Iran** in 1919.

27 Being a poet **Dylan Thomas** (1914) could write his own birthday greeting: 'My birthday began with the water birds and the birds of the winged trees flying my name.' *(Birthday in October).*
Choking back the envy are **John Cleese** (1939), reporter **Sue Lloyd Roberts** (1951) and pop-artist **Roy Lichtenstein** (1923).

28 Witty, bitter **Evelyn Waugh** (1903) wrote *Brideshead Revisited, Decline & Fall, Vile Bodies.*
South African **Harry Oppenheimer** (1908) is one of the world's richest men. Gold, coal, copper . . . he adopted the slogan *Diamonds are Forever* (his empire controls 80% of them).
Lighter-weights **David Dimbleby** (1938) and **Cleo Laine** (1927).

29 'Magic casements, opening on the foam,/Of perilous seas in faery lands forlorn,' lead us to the poet **John Keats** (1795) – although he may really be October 31. As a Scorpio touch, he was apprenticed to an apothecary-surgeon. Died when only 26 of consumption, in dire poverty.

30 **Ezra Pound** (1885), influential US poet. In World War II, broadcast fascist propaganda and was indicted for treason. Appropriately for the time of year he wrote: 'Winter is icummen in,/Lhude sing Goddamm./Raineth drop and staineth slop,/And how the wind doth ramm!/Sing Goddamm.'
Margaret Powell (1907) would laugh anyway!

31

Dick Francis (1920) writes thrillers with sporting backgrounds, and was himself a steeplechase rider. More thrills from **H. R. F. Keating** (1926) and his Inspector Ghote. These are set in India and he wrote 8 before he even went there!
Stage star **Ethel Waters** (1900) travelled as gospel singer in Billy Graham's crusades.

1

Solitary, eccentric **L. S. Lowry** (1887) painted 'matchstick men and dogs' in drab Black Country streets.
Golfer **Gary Player** (1936) won because, 'he likes to beat people' and has a regimen of hard work, self-denial and wheat-germ pills, plus the *Bible, The Power of Positive Thinking* and *Yoga & Health!*

2

Sir John Sainsbury (1927) has transformed the family firm into the country's most successful grocers, worth over a billion pounds. Every inch of floor-space has to earn its keep – which is why our check-outs are like narrow rat runs presumably (snarl!).
Marie Antoinette (1755), Scorpio-aristo to the end.

3

Princess Margaret's son **Viscount Linley** (1961) finds himself in a hotbed of Scorpios – **Ludovic Kennedy** (1919), boxer **Larry Holmes** (1949), novelist of ever-increasing horror **Daoma Winston** (1922) and 'twin', actor **Charles Bronson,** singer **Lulu** (1948), **Ford Sterling** (1880) chief of the original Keystone Cops and **Adam** (1954) without the Ants.

4

Walter Cronkite (1916) American reporter and famous anchorman of *CBS Evening News* 1962-1981. **Will Rogers** (1879), American philosopher and friend, had enough political clout to get Franklin D. Roosevelt elected but said, 'Politics has got so expensive that it takes a lot of money to even get beat with!'

5

Actresses **Tatum O'Neal** (1963) and lovely **Vivien Leigh** (1913) who 'made life hell for everybody near her unless they did everything she wished as she wished and when she wished' – born to be Scarlett O'Hara!
Lester Piggott (1935) the best, the richest, the most difficult jockey on the race-track.

6

The king of the march tune, **John Philip Sousa** (1854), rouses everyone and the birthday has begun!
Busy joining in as well are comedian **Frank Carson** (1926), writer/actor **Donald Churchill** (1930), director/comedian **Mike Nichols** (1931), model **Jean Shrimpton** (1941), TV journalist **Jim Rosenthal** (1947) and actor **Nigel Havers** (1949).

7

Billy Graham (1918), American evangelist. **Joan Sutherland** (1926), Australian prima donna. **Marie Curie** (1867), Polish chemist, discoverer of radium. **Joni Mitchell** (1943), Candian folksinger. **Peter Woods** (1930), English freelance TV presenter. **Albert Camus** (1913), French philosopher who wrote chiefly about the meaninglessness of existence . . . (sigh) but why go on?

8 **Jerome Hines** (1921), American bass. Before singing *Boris Godunov* he prepared a psychiatric study of Boris's mental derangement and so gave an authentic portrayal of manic depression. **Bram Stoker** (1847) was pretty authentic with Count Dracula, vampire . . .
Come in **Ken Dodd** (1927) with your tickling sticks and diddymen – quick!

9 **Lou Ferrigno** (1951), the Incredible Hulk, former Mr America, Mr World and Mr Universe. **King Edward VII** (1841) was a stout gentleman but no match, no match at all. **Carl Sagan** (1934) US astronomer and science populariser, ignores the Hulk and advocates the search for extra-terrestial intelligence.

10 **Vachel Lindsay** (1879) was, by profession, a poet, but he gave recitals of his work and chanted and sang his rhythmic and onomatopoeic pieces like *General William Booth Enters Into Heaven,* in a way to have quite eclipsed actor **Richard Burton** (1925). On the ladies' library list – **Elizabeth Cadell** (1903).

11 Here's comedy actress **June Whitfield** and astrologer **Katina Theodosiou** (1916), then we go into politics with **Roy Jenkins** (1920), and the late **Ian McLeod** (1913) before sinking to **Lucky Luciano** (1896), Grand Master of the Mafia – 'One of the most vicious criminals who ever appeared in this Court,' commented the sentencing Judge.

12 **Princess Grace** of Monaco (1928), formerly film star Grace Kelly. After her death in a car crash in 1982, serious representations were made that she should be canonised. However, Scorpios can go to the other extreme like **Charles Manson** (1934), the evil murderer of Sharon Tate and others.

13 **Robert Louis Stevenson** (1850) wrote *Treasure Island* and that Scorpion parable *Dr Jekyll and Mr Hyde,* although his inclusion today is dicey as he swapped birthdays with a little girl who was born on Christmas Day. All of which leaves little space for **Hermione Baddeley** (1906).

14 To include **Prince Charles** (1948) is obligatory. Almost as important to include are **King Hussein** of Jordan (1935); **Pandit Nehru** (1889), first PM of India; French 'twins' for 1840 – artist **Claude Monet** and sculptor **August Rodin; Sir Frederick Banting** (1891), discoverer of insulin; **Aaron Copland** (1900), US composer; and **Shirley Crabtree 'Big Daddy'** (1936), wrestler.

15 **Richmal Crompton** (1890) wrote the *Just William* stories and Princess Anne's son, **Peter Phillips** (1977), shares the day which sounds ominous! Another William, **William Hope Hodgson** (1877) wrote occult fiction including *Carnacki, the Ghost Finder.* From the world of stage entertainment, **Petula Clark** (1934), **Daniel Barenboim** (1942) and **Mantovani.**

16

Comedian **Griff Rhys Jones** (1953), TV reporter **Vaughan Hughes** (1947), actress/announcer **Su Evans** (1951) – and that's enough of the Welsh contingent! On to politics. **John Bright** (1811), radical MP and **Sir Oswald Mosley** (1896) who was once expected to lead Labour but switched to the British Fascists instead.

17

Auberon Waugh (1939) eldest son of Evelyn Waugh. Regarded as the most offensive journalist in modern times. He goes for anyone, and that includes OAPs! Also able to give good accounts of themselves are **John Wells** (1936) and **Peter Cook** (1937) who, like Waugh, gives his hobby as 'gossip'.

18

Satirist **W. S. Gilbert** (1836) of Gilbertansullivan.
Revivalist **Billy Sunday** (1862) couldn't close down Chicago (that toddlin' town) but made thousands of converts counted, perhaps, by pollster **George Gallup** (1901).
Johnny Mercer (1909) wrote popular songs like *Moon River*.
Alan Shepard (1923) was first US astronaut to travel in space (1961).

19

Dick Cavett (1937) famous American member of that new breed, Chat Show Host. Guest: **Mrs Indira Gandhi** (1917), daughter of Pandit Nehru – a strong-arm woman, tough-minded and cold-blooded. Baroness Stocks said Mrs Gandhi's biography revealed a totally unlovable woman, a very private, inscrutable person, a power lover.

20   **Edwin Hubble** (1889), US astronomer, discovered that neighbouring galaxies are careering away from us, thus establishing that the universe is expanding.
Karl Von Frisch (1886), Austrian zoologist, discovered that the 'dances' of bees convey the direction and distance of food sources.
Alistair Cook (1908) would somehow find a link there.

21   **Beryl Bainbridge** (1934). Her books are comic analyses of tortured characters in suburban settings. Characters and situations were experienced in her own fraught childhood. Hitler in *Young Adolph,* is based on her father. That childhood was her impetus to write. Romantic novelist **Patricia Veryan** prefers a rich Regency background.

NOTES

Sagittarius

22 November – 21 December

Sagittarius, the Archer, is portrayed by a mythical beast, the centaur, half man, half horse. Sagittarians are open-minded, optimistic and adaptable – expansive traits in character with their ruling planet, Jupiter, the largest planet in our Solar system.

At best, Sagittarians are god-like creatures, physically strong and athletic, intellectually well above average. It is the sign of the mystic, the visionary – devout, religious and philosophical; the leader of men, the statesman – humanitarian, benevolent and philanthropic. At worst, Sagittarians are social drop-outs – undisciplined, inconstant, irresponsible wanderers.

But, whichever category they most closely resemble, Sagittarians are never dull and never still! The great travellers of the zodiac, if they cannot roam freely physically, they will do so mentally or spiritually because they hate restrictions or limitations of any kind: they are freedom-fighters and freedom-lovers.

Always restless, these sociable, stimulating personalities rarely have the time or the inclination to form deep or lasting friendships although they make friends easily. They tend to treat love as an exciting game and enjoy the fun of flirting but will veer away sharply from any emotional commitment that threatens their cherished independence.

Yet they cut very romantic figures, these dashing, adventurous individuals who are willing to gamble on almost anything except their personal freedom. They do not find it easy to settle down to domesticity and will be off to seek pastures new at the first sign of jealousy or possessiveness. Once captured though (even Centaurs slow down a little with age!), they make passionate but protective mates.

Impulsively generous, they resent the imposition of others and although they will cheerfully give away something because they feel like it, can't stand being expected to do so. Sagittarians like the unexpected: it presents a challenge which they cannot resist. Quick to think up money-making schemes and willing to take a risk or two, their optimism nearly always pays off.

Even when everything seems to point to financial disaster, lady luck lends a hand. If ruin stares a Sagittarian in the face he/she will quickly change direction, start a new project, take on a part-time job (or two), sell his old books to a mate . . . and make a packet because flexibility is his biggest asset.

Basically, though, Sagittarians are not very interested in material security so need jobs that offer scope for intelligence and allow freedom of expression. So, some become academics or follow literary careers; others take up active, outdoor pursuits or those offering travel opportunities and direct contact with the public.

Honest and straightforward, energetic and outgoing, Sagittarians are idealistic and scrupulously fair. But they never seem to lose their somewhat childlike innocence and sense of fun, so can be irresponsibly boisterous, careless and capricious.

Sagittarius is a dual sign and its subjects are constantly changing their attitude, circumstances or mood. They thrive on freedom of action and thought and, like the Archer, set their sights on the stars!

SAGITTARIUS

Planetary Ruler JUPITER
Element/Quality FIRE/MUTABLE
Keywords FREEDOM, OPENNESS, RESTLESSNESS, FAITH
Day THURSDAY
Number 3
Colour PURPLE, AUTUMNAL TINTS
Metal TIN
Stones AMETHYST, CARBUNCLE, BLUE JOHN, TURQUOISE
Countries ARABIA, AUSTRALIA, HUNGARY, SPAIN
Places In Britain: BRADFORD, SHEFFIELD, SUNDERLAND
   Elsewhere: AVIGNON, BUDAPEST, COLOGNE, TOLEDO, TUSCANY,
   SINGAPORE, STUTTGART
Trees/Shrubs OAK, BIRCH, LIME, MULBERRY
Flowers/Herbs ALOE, BORAGE, MOSSES, PINKS, SAGE

22 Still *just* Scorpios: **George Eliot** (1819), even though she looked like a Sagittarian horse, **Benjamin Britten** (1913), **Peter Hall** (1930), **Billie-Jean King** (1943).
Definitely or probably Sagittarians: **General de Gaulle** (1890), **Hoagy Carmichael** and his 'twin', aviator **Wiley Post** (1899), novelist **Elizabeth Renier** (1916) and **John Bird** (1936).

23 The birthday of historical novelist **Nigel Tranter** (1909) and **Harpo Marx** (1888), the completely barmy, girl-chasing one. TV birthday girls he could chase if he were with us today – **Sue Nicholls** (1943) and **Diana Quick** (1946).
To give everyone a fright – **Boris Karloff** (1887) as Frankenstein's Monster.

24 **Henri de Toulouse-Lautrec** (1864) frequented brothels, circuses and music halls, painting posters for posterity.
Scott Joplin (1868), before finding respectability with the *Maple Leaf Rag,* played piano in honky-tonks and gambling halls along the Mississippi.
We cannot answer for cricketers **Ian Botham** (1955) and **Herbert Sutcliffe** (1894).

25 **Poul Anderson** (1926), sci-fi writer, noted for his time-travel ideas. **Pope John XXIII** (1881), portly, humble, universally loved. Patron saint of motorists, **Karl Benz** (1844) built the first feasible automobile. Philanthropists, **Andrew Carnegie** (1835) and **Henry Mayhew** (1812) who compiled the report, *London Labour and the London Poor.*

26 Go to a Trusthouse Forte for the birthday binge and you'll be sharing your celebration with the boss, hotelier and caterer, **Lord Forte** (1908). Knocking back champagne too will be **Pat Phoenix** (1924), **Emlyn Williams** (1905), novelist **Pamela Hill** (1920) and **Charles Schulz** (1922), cartoonist, creator of *Peanuts*.

27 The short, fat legs of **Ernie Wise** (1925) are a disgrace to Sagittarius and we can only hope for long and lissom pins on **Caroline Kennedy** (1957), sci-fi writer **L. Sprague de Camp** (1907) and your friends.
Anders Celsius (1701), Swedish astronomer, devised the centigrade scale of temperature.

28 **William Blake** (1757), artist, poet, mystic, lived in a world of visions, thinking it a commonplace to see a treeful of angels at Peckham Rye. His wife complained, 'I have very little of Mr Blake's company, he is always in Paradise.' Wrote *Jerusalem* – 'Bring me my Bow of Burning Gold. . .'

29 Hundreds of girls arranged in floral patterns, waltzing down staircases, playing grand pianos . . . and we recognize **Busby Berkeley** (1895) director of lush Hollywood musicals. More girls – **Louisa May Alcott** (1832) and her *Little Women*. An old girl, **Gertrude Jekyll** (1843), first of the artistic gardeners, and we've come full circle!

30

Sir Winston Churchill (1874) leads the birthday procession. He had a not unknown 'twin' – Canadian **L. M. Montgomery** who wrote *Anne of Green Gables*. Another schoolgirl favourite was **Angela Brazil** (1868).
Home-spun philosopher and humorist **Mark Twain** (1835) smoked cigars and gambled and was a river pilot on the Mississippi.

1

We can't compete with the United States today. What with **Woody Allen** (1935) winning superlatives from all sides, **Bette Midler** (1945) *(The Divine Miss M)* and **Mary Martin** (1913), star of *South Pacific* and mother of J.R., we might as well put up the shutters. **Keith Michell** (1928) is Australian.

2

Conductor **Sir John Barbirolli** (1899) and his 'twin' **Sir John Cobb,** racing motorist. He was killed while attempting to raise the water speed record. 'Possessed of courage and skill beyond the ordinary, he never allowed his success and its attendant publicity to spoil a friendly and lovable character.'

3

Sir Rowland Hill (1795) introduced the penny post and the adhesive stamp. **Octavia Hill** (1838) was an early social worker and pioneer of London slum clearance.
Author **Nigel Balchin** (1908) wrote *The Small Back Room.*
Entertainers: **Paul Nicholas** (1945), **Moyra Fraser** (1923), **Andy Williams** (1930) and **Mel Smith** (1952).

4   **Deanna Durbin** (1922). The BBC are said to get more requests for her films than anyone else's. Other entertaining ladies are **Gemma Jones** (1942) and **Pamela Stephenson.** On a higher plane altogether, the operatic diva **Maria Callas** (1923). Some jolly gents as escorts are **Ronnie Corbett** (1930) and **Jimmy Jewell** (1912).

5   **Walt Disney** (1901). There is said to be a lot of him in Micky Mouse, the optimistic, fun-loving character who has entertained us for decades. Disney had Sagittarius's attributes of broad vision, willingness to gamble, to advertise and to laugh. A ticket to Disneyland as a super birthday gift?

6   **Ira Gershwin** (1896) lyricist to brother George, whisked up the words of *Love Walked Right In, A Foggy Day in London Town, Fascinatin' Rhythm.* **Sir Osbert Sitwell** (1892) could too: 'On the Coast of Coromandel, Dance they to the tunes of Handel. . .' **Will Hay** (1888) was a comedian and astronomer.

7   Two 'bodice buster' authors – **Rosemary Rogers** (1932) penner of the 600 odd pages of *Sweet, Savage Love* and **Christopher Nicole** (1930) whose historical novels are set in the West Indies – lots of rapes and floggings as in *Mistress of Darkness*. For aged romantics, **Rudolf Friml** (1879), composer of *Rose Marie.*

8 Humorist **James Thurber** (1894) was Sagittarius with Moon in Aries and he got along fine with folk born between 20th/24th August. 'Quick to arouse, he is very hard to quiet and people often just go away.'
Another Sagittarian born today with the Moon in Aries is actress **Jennie Linden** (1940).

9 Ladies born today include coloratura soprano **Elizabeth Schwarzkopf** (1915), **Hermione Gingold** (1897), **Judi Dench** (1934) and novelist **Joanna Trollope** (1943). Athletic Sagittarian gentlemen are **Douglas Fairbanks Jnr** (1909), **Kirk Douglas** (1916), **Neil Innes** (1944), **Clarence Birdseye** (1886) who invented a quick-freeze process, and waltzing **Waldteufel** (1837).

10 **George MacDonald** (1824) wrote children's fiction like *The Princess and The Goblin* and allegorical fantasies set in dream/mirror worlds. **Rumer Godden** (1907) frequently writes of her 'other home', India. **Emily Dickinson** (1830) rarely stirred from the family home at Amherst but her poetry ranged over and beyond the universe.

11 **Annie Jump Cannon** (1863) – what extraordinary names Americans have! – astronomer, the 'Census Taker of the Sky'.
John Larson (1892) invented the lie detector. His 'twin' **Ursula Bloom,** *au contraire,* spun hundreds of romances.
Wealthy **Christina Onassis** (1950). Russian **Aleksandr Solzhenitsyn** (1918).
Composer **Hector Berlioz** (1803). Commentator **Cliff Michelmore** (1919).

12
Author **John Osborne** (1929).
Classy singers **Dionne Warwick** (1941), **Connie Francis** (1938), **Frank Sinatra** (1915). Filmstar **Edward G. Robinson** (1893) excelled in gangster roles – they don't breed 'em like that any more; say what you will about **Lionel Blair** (1932), **Kenneth Cranham** (1944) and **Barrie Rutter** (1946)!

13
Author **Laurens van der Post** (1906) usually gives his books (like *Flamingo Feather*) vivid African backgrounds. They are concerned with war, social tensions, exploration, adventure. He has been on several Government missions and is in with the Top Brass. On the lighter side, actor **Dick van Dyke** (1925).

14
King George VI (1895).
Actress **Lee Remick** (1935).
Shirley Jackson (1919) writes fantasy and horror stories like *The Haunting of Hill House* but don't be scared. The gothic atmosphere will be dispelled by maniacal **Spike Jones** (1911) and his City Slickers screaming for *Chloe (You old bat!)*.

15
J. Paul Getty (1892) was the world's wealthiest man – from oil – although you would never have thought it.
Engineer **Alexandre Eiffel** (1832) built the tower which bears his name.
Edna O'Brien (1930) is the archetypal wild but captivating Irish colleen. She was established with her first book, *The Country Girls*.

16 Some giants today: **Ludwig van Beethoven** (1770). **Jane Austen** (1775). Religious poet, *The Hound of Heaven,* **Francis Thompson** (1859). Philosopher **George Santayana** (1863). Hungarian composer **Zoltan Kodaly** (1882) and 'twin' the cricketer **J. B. Hobbs.** **Noel Coward** (1899). **V. S. Pritchett** (1900). American anthropologist **Margaret Mead** (1901). Prophet **Arthur C. Clarke** (1917).

17 **Robert Robinson** (1927) welcomes present and past celebrants. Theatricals: **Tommy Steele** (1936), **Christopher Cazenove** (1945) and **J. Robertson** ('Oh, Calamity!') **Hare** (1891).
Alison Uttley (1884) who wrote *Little Grey Rabbit.*
Sir Humphrey Davy (1778), physicist and lionized lecturer who bounded about in ecstacy when his experiments worked and – discovered laughing gas!

18 Dramatist **Christopher Fry** (1907) is irresistible. He wrote *Venus Observed,* chockful of astrological allusions. Equally irresistible are clown **Joseph Grimaldi** (1778), politician **Willy Brandt** (1913), writers **Saki** (1870), **Michael Moorcock** (1939) and **Jill Tattersall** (1931), actresses **Gladys Cooper** (1888), **Celia Johnson** (1908), **Betty Grable** (1916) and miscellaneous **Lord Lucan** (1934).

19 **Eleanor Porter** (1868) created Pollyanna the girl who saw the silver lining to even the blackest cloud. The other comedian for the day is **Syd Little** (1942).
Other celebrities include **Sir Ralph Richardson** (1902), **Edith Piaf** (1919), **Eamonn Andrews** (1922) and **Gordon Jackson** (1923), Hudson in *Upstairs, Downstairs.*

20 Dan Leno (1860) clown, acrobat and clog dancer, had a comical, rubbery face. 'I defy anyone not to have loved him at first sight,' said Max Beerbohm.
Walter Adams (1876), US astronomer, made first discovery of white dwarf star. Uri Geller (1946) is, apparently, on terms with beings 'out there'!

21 What with actress Jane Fonda (1937) limbering up wherever you look, Chris Evert Lloyd (1954) practising smash hits, Walter Hagen (1892), a sparkling, carefree personality, driving straight down the fairway, there's barely room for today's giant statesman Benjamin Disraeli (1804) the audaciously brilliant character who made Victoria Empress of India.

NOTES

Capricorn

22 December – 20 January

Capricorn is ruled by sombre Saturn, the planet of responsibility, limitation and stability. Natives of this sign are reliable, prudent and cautious, they are also very practical, efficient and determined to achieve the status they feel is their due.

They are self-sufficient and can endure adversity nobly. Which is probably just as well because many of them take time to recover from a deprived or father-dominated childhood. Often shy and timid in their teens, Capricornians don't emerge as strong-minded, capable individuals until into their twenties or thirties.

Capricornians do, however, flourish in maturity and if good-looking – which many of them are – stay good-looking. Happily, too, although seemingly old in their youth, they become youthful in their old age: a sort of reversal of the ageing process! Perhaps thanks to Saturn, the planet associated with old age, those born under the sign of the Goat are survivors.

They may appear to be reserved, pleasant folk of few words but are strong and tough. Capricornians are extremely industrious and, slowly but surely, achieve whatever they have set as their goal. Very ambitious, they don't usually even contemplate marriage until they are settled in their careers, or at least until they have a hoof on the first rung!

When they do finally get around to marriage, Capricornians make faithful spouses and good, caring parents. Naturally rather inhibited, they do not give their love easily or quickly but, once they have given their hearts, are steadfast in their devotion. And, beneath that serious exterior lurks an exciting lover, warm and sensual, who will respond to affection with passion and humour.

For, despite their reserved manner, Capricornians have a pronounced sense of humour and their somewhat droll wit can make them delightful and amusing companions. They are reliable and dependable in all their relationships and others will always know where they stand because the Goat tribe keep their word implicitly.

However, they may also be rather rigid in outlook and can, on occasion, be real wet blankets because they are worriers and prone to depression. And, if they are feeling in sombre mood, it won't matter what you suggest to liven them up. Just leave them alone to think things through on their own: they need time to assimilate new ideas or attitudes.

It usually takes time, too, for Capricornians to reach the top of their chosen profession. Self-confident and strong-willed, practical and methodical, they take most things in their stride and work steadily, determinedly towards their goal. Sometimes their careers take on so much importance that they have little time for socialising or for leisure activities: they can become workaholics!

But the get-rich-quick scheme, the speculative venture or outright gamble simply does not appeal to the Capricornian temperament. Politics, the law or government may attract these ambitious people, though, for they are not averse to being in the public eye. But, whether in big business or small, they have natural authority, dignity and scrupulous honesty. Mentally acute, they also have financial ability and it is rare to find a member of the Goat tribe who leaves this world poorer than he/she entered it!

CAPRICORN

Planetary Ruler   SATURN
Element/Quality   EARTH/CARDINAL
Keywords   STATUS, CAUTION, RELIABILITY, AMBITION
Day   SATURDAY
Number   8
Colour   VANDYKE BROWN, BLACK, GREY
Metal   LEAD/PEWTER
Stones   ONYX, JET, GARNET, SAPPHIRE, TIGER'S EYE
Countries   ALBANIA, BULGARIA, INDIA, GREECE, MEXICO
Places   In Britain: KEITHLEY, OXFORD, ORKNEY AND SHETLAND ISLES
   Elsewhere: BRANDENBURG, BRUSSELS, PORT SAID, SAXONY
Trees/Shrubs   YEW, WILLOW, ELM, ASPEN, PINE
Flowers/Herbs   HELLEBORE, HENBANE, HEMLOCK, FOXGLOVE,
   SAGE, PANSY, SNOWDROP

♑

22 Capricorn claims DJ **Noel Edmonds** (1948) and, probably, the 6th **Duke of Westminster** (1951) who is reckoned to be worth 600 million pounds, and 1937 'twins' **Charlotte Lamb** and **David Case,** prolific multi-pen-named authors. She publishes a romance a month, he writes horror and porn. Both are very rich.

23 **Yousuf Karsh** (1908) photographed all the top men, like Hemingway and Churchill, in a very dignified manner. The results were technically perfect but static.
Samuel Smiles (1812) wrote the Victorian/Capricorn Bible, *Self-Help* and said, 'Active work is always attended by happiness' – which can be taken as today's motto.

24 Billionaire **Howard Hughes** (1905) was dominated by his father, Texan oilman Howard Hughes senior, and became a phobia-ridden recluse. **Matthew Arnold** (1822) was also overawed by his father (Dr Arnold of Rugby). He was a poet, famous for *Dover Beach,* and a school inspector. Providing the beauty, **Ava Gardner** (1922).

25 Concentrating on earthly status, we have **Princess Alexandra** (1936), **Princess Alice,** the **Duchess of Gloucester** (1901), **Helena Rubinstein** (1872), **Conrad Hilton** (1887) and **Humphrey Bogart** (1899) who took the unsentimental, disenchanted Capricorn roles and, 'looked battered before anything had happened, as if survival at an honourable wage was all he hoped for.'

26 **Irene Handl** (1902). Her mother died young and Irene kept house for her father until she was in her 30s when she at last realized her ambition to go on the stage. Actor **Denis Quilley** (1927) and actress/singer **Toni Arthur** (1941) didn't have to wait so long.

27 **Louis Pasteur** (1822), French chemist, discovered germs and pursued them single-mindedly with innoculation and pasteurisation. A mediocre schoolboy, he matured late as many Capricorns do. Never forsook his lowly upbringing (father was a tanner). And, if you're wrinkling your pretty nose, here's glamorous-at-any-age **Marlene Dietrich** (1901).

28 The good-looking birthday girls first. Besides your friends there's actresses **Hildegarde Neff** (1925) and **Maggie Smith** (1934). Representing high society, **Princess Yasmin** (1950) daughter of Prince Ali Khan and Rita Hayworth.
Representing politics, **Roy Hattersley** (1932) Deputy Leader of the Labour Party.
Presenting everyone, TV's **Richard Whiteley** (1943).

29 Capricorn's GOM is **William Ewart Gladstone** (1809). Prime Minister four times, the last when 83. 'His hawk's eye was terrible as an army in battle, his deep bass voice inspired awe.' Hobbies: rescuing fallen women and felling trees. He should have met the politically influential **Marquise de Pompadour** (1721), mistress of Louis XV!

♑

30 Today's top birthday: **Rudyard Kipling** (1865), jingoist and Just-So Storyteller. A miserable childhood resulted in a lifelong feeling of desertion. Practised the Capricorn Code of moral obligation, worldly wisdom, travelling alone and keeping your head when all about you . . . 'He didn't seem able to take things lightly,' said Lady Astor.

31 **Elizabeth Arden** (1878), a thorough-going martinet Capricorn. Advocated hygiene, exercise and correct posture as well as her cosmetics. Fashion designer **Diane von Furstenberg** (1946) also turned herself into a multimillion dollar concern. Popularised the simple but sexy jersey dress, marketed cosmetics *and* wrote a *Book of Beauty*.

JANUARY

1 **Maria Edgeworth** (1767) wrote *Edgeworth's Early Lessons*, popular nursery tales designed to avoid inflaming young imaginations or exciting a restless spirit of adventure by exhibiting false views of life. Heedless **Joe Orton** (1933) wrote black comedies like *Entertaining Mr Sloane* and, as a Saturnian moral, was murdered by his lover.

2 **Isaac Asimov** (1920), the sci-fi writer, exudes confidence. He attributes this to living so much inside his own head and being so unaware of the outside world that when he seems to be utterly self-possessed he is really unaware that there's anything to be disturbed about!

3

J. R. R. Tolkien (1892) created his own world in that scholarly fairytale *The Lord of the Rings*. Died at 81 surrounded by hobbits.
Victoria Principal alias Pam Ewing, was one of Patrick Lichfield's 'most beautiful women' and made a commercial success of her beauty and fitness business.

4

Artist **Augustus John** (1878). 'His natural grandeur,' to quote Cecil Beaton, 'rather than diminishing with age, attained such stature that long before his death he became monumental.' Comforting for your elderly birthday relations!
Actress **Barbara Rush** (1928).
Learned professor **Jacob Grimm** (1785), one of the Brothers Grimm who wrote the fairy tales.

5

Actress **Pamela Sue Martin** (1954), alias Fallon Carrington in *Dynasty*, has Capricorn's civic conscience – she is an active member of Greenpeace.
Stella Gibbons (1902) wrote the hilarious *Cold Comfort Farm*, an apt title to come from Saturn's sign.
Newsreader **Jan Leeming** (1942) gives her hobby as – work!

6

John De Lorean (1923), a brilliant engineer, attained the corridors of power and a glittering life-style. Seemed all set to develop his own automobile company but, alas, pride went before a fall. **Rowan Atkinson** (1955) trained as an electrical engineer but, far from taking over Telecom, went into acting.

7

Saint Bernadette (1844), peasant girl who claimed to have seen the Virgin Mary at Lourdes which started the pilgrimages to that town.
Zoologist and conservationist **Gerald Durrell** (1925) wrote *The Overloaded Ark*, etc. Capricorn comes out strongly for ecology, probably because of its appreciation of a natural hierarchy.

8

Swinging, singing **Shirley Bassey** (1937) and **Elvis Presley** (1935). He was a very solitary figure despite being king of rock-and-roll.
As birthday companions for older friends there's **Dennis Wheatley** (1897), author of historical and supernatural novels, and occultist **Madeline Montalban** (1910), a stalwart of *Prediction* for years.

9

Capricorn is a sign which traditionally improves with keeping, so here's **Clive Dunn** (1922), best known for his 'old man' roles, especially in *Bootsie and Snudge, Dad's Army* and his song *Grandad,* and **Gracie Fields** (1898) who went on for ever as blithe on Capri as she was in Rochdale.

10

Capricorn is a heavy sign and it's not surprising to find here sculptor **Barbara Hepworth** (1903). She liked her massive pieces to be touched – it's an ancient, pagan feeling – thrived on hard work and found the sound of the mallet 'music to her ears.' For today's clown – **Grock** (1880).

11 Gordon Selfridge (1864), shopkeeper, pulled down £90,000 p.a. 'Push and hard work are all you need.' Philosopher **William James** (1842) wrote *Principles of Psychology*. **Lord Curzon** (1859) was Viceroy of India. **Alan Paton** (1903) wrote *Cry, the Beloved Country*, a very *worthy* book. A serious day if it wasn't for. . .?

12 Celebrating today are **Michael Aspel** (1933) and **Des O'Connor** (1932). Pre-TV there's high society boxer **Georges Carpentier** (1894), high society portrait painter **John Singer Sargent** (1856), high society danceband leader **Harry Roy,** high society actress **Luise Rainer** (1912), high society speakeasy hostess **Texas** 'Hello sucker!' **Guinan** (1884).

13 Thoroughbred **Kay Francis** (1903) was Hollywood's best-dressed actress. Elegant **Oliver Messel** (1904) designed stage sets and costumes at all the Covent Garden and Glyndebourne galas and also the initial building development on Mustique. Stumping along behind, complete with safety pin, comes Paddington Bear with his chronicler **Michael Bond** (1926).

14 More elegance! **Cecil Beaton** (1904). *My Fair Lady's* black and white Ascot put the popular seal on his long career as photographer, designer and author. Actress **Faye Dunaway** (1941) always wanted to be 'best' and is noted for total commitment to her profession, classic features and flair for clothes.

15 **Aristotle Onassis** (1906) had made his first million by his 25th birthday (dig!). In the marble halls of Eaton Square there's **Lord Lever** (1914) socialist millionaire. Still with the nobs, **Marie Duplessis** (1824), high-class tart, Dumas' *La Dame Aux Camelias*, and **Mazo de la Roche** (1879) who created the Whiteoaks family.

16 **Robert Service** (1876) educated in the College of Hard Knocks, wrote that famous piece *The Shooting of Dan McGrew*. 'Back of the bar, in a solo game, sat Dangerous Dan McGrew; And watching his luck was his light o' love, the lady that's known as Lou. . .' **Ethel Merman** (1901) we bet!

17 'Scarface' **Al Capone** (1899) controlled all 10,000 speakeasies in Chicago by 1925. 'Everybody calls me a racketeer' he complained. 'I call myself a businessman.' **Vidal Sassoon** (1928), under the fancy coiffure, is also a businessman with expensive international schools of hairdressing.
Ballerina **Moira Shearer** (1926) had lovely red-gold hair.

18 **A. A. Milne** (1882) throws the birthday binge for Christopher Robin and Pooh. Guests include **Arthur Ransome** (1884) with his *Swallows and Amazons,* and **David Bellamy** (1933) who flounders in from a bog, with waterweed in his beard and a pocketful of newts. Being Capricorn he's a very serious conservationist.

19 Other mothers besides **Michael Crawford's** (1942) 'ad 'em today!
Crime novelist and 'loner' **Patricia Highsmith** (1921); spine-chilling **Edgar Allan Poe** (1809); misanthropic **Paul Cezanne** (1839) who painted in cubes of colour; fortissimo **Janis Joplin** (1943) and **Dolly Parton** (1946) who just isn't the right shape for Capricorn!

20 **Joy Adamson** (1910), wild life conservationist. 13 million people bought her three 'Elsa' books.
Patricia Neal (1926), actress, suffered a stroke and long coma after a series of domestic tragedies. Brought back to life almost single-handed by husband Roald Dahl – a cheering example of Capricorn resilience.

NOTES

Aquarius

21 January – 19 February

As everyone knows, we are entering the Age of Aquarius and people born under the sign of the Water Bearer should feel at home, even if nobody else does! It is the freak influence of Uranus, the planet of originality, inspiration and eccentricity, that makes Aquarius so contrary.

They are the non-conformists of the zodiac, the unconventionals, the 'mods' with meaningful relationships which end up not meaning much, the politically and community minded. Aquarians usually support the left – unless, that is, the left happens to be in power and then, of course, they will veer to the right because they tend to identify with the underdog.

Notoriously unsnobbish, they enjoy mixing with others and, as they have bubbling, witty and vivacious personalities, can be the life and soul of any party. Restless and curious, anything unusual or new will capture their interest, so they are attracted to the latest fashions and possess an aloof glamour that is both fascinating and dynamic.

But beneath that confident exterior lurks a seething mass of indecision and anxiety that can lead to contradictory displays of temperament. On occasion quiet, even silent in their anger, they can be very stubborn and, once having taken a stance about something, are seldom persuaded that they are wrong. Not that they are unduly concerned by what others think of them anyway!

Aquarians are natural rebels and delight in being slightly – even jarringly – out of step with their peers, so certainly aren't prepared to alter their opinions or behaviour simply in order to conform to society's dictates. If this sounds a little perverse, a bit eccentric, well – it's all due to the Aquarian passion for originality, for personal freedom: an attitude that extends to all areas of life – clothes, life-style, even relationships.

Most of them are, however, in tune with modern science, with technology, and are interested in any form of new equipment or device that has been or is being developed or invented to assist man in his life on earth . . . or in space. Aquarians spend many pleasant hours reading and studying a wide range of progressive subjects and, often, take up unusual hobbies or professions.

They may be inventors, analysts, economists, disporters of themselves in Think Tanks, mathematicians, micro-chip experts, child prodigies; psychiatrists, sociologists, aviators, cosmonauts, explorers or electricians. Their spare time may be spent radio hamming, potholing or hang-gliding to raise money for charity.

Literary Aquarians write science fiction, social studies and experimental novels; the artists are decidedly *avant-garde* the composers are other-worldly. Some of these subjects are really wacky and become astrologers, for Aquarius is the astrologer's sign.

It is also known as the sign of genius and those born under it are intelligent, original and inventive individuals who are passionately interested in tomorrow. They have a great belief in mankind's future and its ability to surmount the difficulties of the environment aided, of course, by heart-stoppingly handsome, bursting with brains, crammed with charisma . . . Aquarians!

AQUARIUS

Planetary Ruler　URANUS
Element/Quality　AIR/FIXED
Keywords　INDEPENDENCE, OPTIMISM, HUMANITY, INITIATIVE
Day　SATURDAY
Number　4
Colour　ELECTRIC BLUE, BRIGHT PINK, PALE GREEN
Metal　LEAD/PEWTER
Stones　TURQUOISE, SAPPHIRE, CHALCEDONY, AMETHYST
Countries　ABYSSINIA, AFGHANISTAN, RED RUSSIA, SWEDEN
Places　In Britain: BRIGHTON, SALISBURY, TRENT
　Elsewhere: BREMEN, PIEDMONT, HAMBURG, SALTZBURG
Trees/Shrubs　LIME, FRUIT TREES
Flowers/Herbs　HYDRANGEA, ROSEMARY, PARSLEY, PRIMROSE,
　SMALL WATER PLANTS

≋

21 Those born today should be fashion-plates as they are in the company of **Christian Dior** (1905) and **Cristobal Balenciaga** (1895). The former's New Look revolutionized dress in 1945. Golfer **Jack Nicklaus** (1940) is a snazzy dresser, so are opera singer **Placido Domingo** (1941) and actor **Telly Savalas** (1923).

22 **Lord Byron** (1788) was 'mad, bad and dangerous to know'; an aristocratic revolutionary; a darkly romantic, crippled roué; an Aquarian lady's dream!
Claire Rayner (1931) would have sorted him out! An outspoken, frighteningly efficient lady – ex-nurse, novelist, agony aunt . . . Another agony aunt – **Peggy Makins (Evelyn Home)** (1916).

23 **Princess Caroline** of Monaco (1956) sounds a headstrong, wilful Aquarian from all accounts, so we had better counter her with **Lord Denning,** Master of the Rolls (1899) – although, come to think of it, he insisted that the law must move with the times and made more controversial judgments than anyone.

24 Zoologist **Desmond Morris** (1928) researched first animal behaviour and then the human variety. An individualist, he wants more excitement in zoos and in our own lives. Society is in danger of becoming homogenised, sensible and systematised. 'Damm the system! Bring back the oddities!' Not at all homogenised are **Neil Diamond** (1941) and **Earl Spencer** (1924).

25 Experimental novelist **Virginia Woolf** (1882) of the elegantly strange Aquarian looks; a left-winger and women's libber.
Somerset Maugham (1874), cynical student of human nature with an Aquarian private life.
Robert Burns (1759) scandalised his sanctimonious neighbours and touted the French Revolution and free love.

26 Black, militant communist **Angela Davis** (1944); **Baroness Von Trappe** (1905) who had a most adventurous life and became the inspiration for *The Sound of Music;* the beautifully Aquarian-voiced cellist **Jacqueline du Pre** (1945) and **Eartha Kitt** (1928). Eartha's 'twin' **Roger Vadim;** Jacqueline's, **Marti Caine.** Actor **Paul Newman** (1925).

27 **Wolfgang Amadeus Mozart** (1756) and **Lewis Carroll** (1832). Mozart's music is the essence of civilised Aquarian elegance; Carroll, an Oxford don, caricatured himself as that charming oddity and inventor, the White Knight.
Albert Watkins (1855) was also an inventor, photographer, politician, conjurer, skater – and discoverer of the mysterious ley lines.

28 **Colette** (1873), author of the enchanting *Gigi,* had all the *chic* of her nation and sign.
Jackson Pollock (1912) communist and *avant-garde* artist, pegged his canvases on the floor and poured paint on them from a scaffold.
General 'Chinese' Gordon (1833).
All had funny-peculiar Aquarian lives.

29 **Germaine Greer** (1939) 6ft of disturbing intelligence and beauty, anarchist, atheist, women's libber, underground journalist, singer, dancer, actress – 'I was always a freak' – acid-penned author of *The Female Eunuch*. Plus **John Junkin** (1930), star of stage, screen etc. . . . whose hobbies include crosswords, quizzes and 'plotting to overthrow Willie Rushton.'

30 Actress **Vanessa Redgrave** (1937), alias the Workers Revolutionary Party, is dedicated to abolishing the monarchy and capitalism by armed insurrection if necessary. A nicely brought-up girl too!
Franklin D. Roosevelt (1882), President of the United States, said, 'A radical is a man with his feet firmly planted in the air!'

31 **Beatrix of Holland** (1938), an independent, autocratic monarch. *Enfants terribles:* **Tallulah Bankhead** (1902), **Mario Lanza** (1921), **Norman Mailer** (1923).
Franz Schubert (1797), whose music is 'compressed lyrical insanity,' said he should be kept by the State.
Pacifist preacher **Lord Soper** (1903) was often knocked off Tower Hill wall!

FEBRUARY

1 **Stephen Potter** (1900) invented Gamesmanship – how to win without actually cheating. Not needed, surely, by soprano **Renata Tebaldi** (1922) of the exquisitely cool, pure voice, massive contralto **Clara Butt** (1873), novelist **Denise Robins** (1897), her novelist daughter **Patricia Robins/Claire Lorrimer** (1921) or actor **Clark Gable** (1901).

2

Leading the field, **Farah Fawcett** (1947), **Elaine Stritch** (1925), **Libby Purves** (1950) and **Margot Asquith** (1864), an outrageous, political hostess who looked like 'two profiles stuck together.'
James Joyce (1882), literary anarchist, psychoanalyst's delight, author of the incomprehensible *Ulysses* and *Finnegan's Wake* squeezes in. So does comedian **Les Dawson** (1934).

3

Gertrude Stein (1874) is either accounted a genius or downright peculiar. She wrote, 'A rose is a rose is a rose.'
Felix Mendelssohn (1809) was charming and his music perfection. Precocious and animated, he hated vagueness and his work is orderly, neat and not over-impassioned.
Walter Bagehot (1826) political analyst.

4

Betty Friedan (1921) wrote *The Feminine Mystique* and revived the feminist movement in the States in the 60s. But you can't keep the men – chauvinists that they are – out. Without even trying they lob across **Charles Lindbergh** (1902) who flew the Atlantic solo in an animated chicken coop.

5

This hurts but, sourly, we include successful TV astrologer **Russell Grant** (1951) who is ever so flamboyant and ever so fat! – partnered by **Belle Starr** (1848), celebrated female outlaw of the Wild West. She wore velvet gowns and riding boots. He sports rainbow wellies. *She* was ambushed and done in . . .

6
Head-turning Aquarian actresses **Zsa-Zsa Gabor** (1921), **Mamie van Doren** (1933) and **Gayle Hunnicut** (1943) have to have their birthdays remembered today. And actor **Patrick MacNee** (1922) twinned with **Denis Norden. Frank Muir** (1920) was yesterday. And, of course, forsaking films for politics, **President Ronald Reagan** (1911).

7
Twin comediennes for 1924, **Dora Bryan** and **Hattie Jacques,** she of the authentic, clear, light Aquarian voice.
Charles Dickens (1812) had a penchant for actresses and would have adored both. He was a genius and social reformer and could have stood for Parliament but, thank goodness, wrote *Pickwick.*

8
Evangeline Adams (1868) was with-it and made the world's first astrology broadcast.
Chester Carlson (1906) invented Xerox.
Jules Verne (1828) kept abreast of the latest scientific developments and anticipated TV, space travel, submarines, aqualungs etc. His books, like *Twenty Thousand Leagues Under The Sea,* proved amazingly far-sighted.

9
Fashionable, aristocratic **Anthony Hope** (1863), author of *The Prisoner of Zenda.*
Aristocratic, fashionable **Ronald Colman** (1891) starred in a film version with devasting results for the female audiences.
Aquarian actresses **Mia Farrow** (1945), **Janet Suzman** (1939), **Carmen Miranda** (1904) and the witty but difficult **Mrs Patrick Campbell** (1865).

10   **Joyce Grenfell** (1910) was pure Aquarian in voice and looks – 'the sort of face you see in the back of a spoon.' Very superior **Bertolt Brecht** (1898) wrote *The Threepenny Opera* and remarked, 'I am not writing for the scum who want to have the cockles of their hearts warmed.' Ouch!

11   **Mary Quant** (1934) invented the Chelsea Look in the Swinging Sixties. Now 'into' cosmetics which are easily recognisable in their jazzy, magpie, Aquarian packaging. **W. H. Fox Talbot** (1800), pioneer of photography, perfected a negative from which any number of prints could be made. **Thomas Alva Edison** (1847) invented everything else.

12   1809 'twins' **Abraham Lincoln** and **Charles Darwin.** Lincoln delivered that Aquarian manifesto the *Gettysburg Address* and was assassinated. Darwin wrote the evolutionary bombshell, *Origin of Species* and was denounced as an unprincipled atheist by the Church and a flaming liar by the common herd – especially the very hirsute ones.

13   **Georges Simenon** (1903), Maigret's creator, is a modern, sociological writer, a detached recorder without sentiment or prejudice.
Lord Randolph Churchill (1849), Winston's father, was 'a left-wing Conservative . . . an unconscious rebel against his own environment . . . a Bohemian aristocrat.'
Actor **Oliver Reed** (1938) doesn't seem like the rest of us either.

14 1913 'twins' – **Bishop James Pike** and US Labour leader **James Hoffa.** Both met mysterious ends. The Bishop in the Judean desert, while Hoffa was last seen in a car park before lunching with 3 alleged hoodlums. Worse follows! **Frank Harris** (1856) wrote the shocking *My Life and Loves* in 3 volumes.

15 **Charles Tiffany** (1812) founded Tiffany & Co. **Henry Steinway** (1797) founded Steinway & Sons.
Sax Rohmer (1883) founded Dr Fu Manchu, the sinister Oriental criminal.
Pausing only for a stifled scream, here's luminous actress **Claire Bloom** (1931) and actor **John Barrymore** (1882), another 'mad, bad and dangerous to know' Aquarian.

16 Alone, on centre court, superbrat **John McEnroe** (1959).
Scientific representatives for the day are Dutch botanist **Hugo de Vries** (1845) and English **Sir Francis Galton** (1822). The former's theory was that evolution could be by-passed by a new species arriving overnight; the latter pioneered fingerprint identification.

17 **The Reverend Thomas Malthus** (1766) published an *Essay on the Principle of Population as it Affects the Future Improvement of Society* which proved to be another Aquarian bombshell.
If Malthus is too erudite for your circle, here's Dame Edna Everage, superstar, with her dogsbody **Barry Humphries** (1934) in the background.

18 **Yoko Ono** (1933) married John Lennon and allegedly made a film composed entirely of bare bottoms. Your friends can't possibly be more Aquarian than Yoko.
Quite an electrically charged birthday containing also **John Travolta** (1954) and **Alessandro Volta** (1745) pioneer of electricity – good old volt himself!

19 Those born today 'come under' either Aquarius or Pisces depending on date, time and place. Definitely Aquarius is Tasmanian born film star **Merle Oberon** (1911) – she was in *Wuthering Heights* in 1939. Definitely Pisces, **Prince Andrew** (1960). Don't knows: **Stan Kenton** (1912), jazz band leader, and actor **Lee Marvin** (1924).

NOTES

Pisces

20 February - 21 March

The sign of the Fishes is ruled by Neptune, the planet associated with the subconscious mind, with mysticism, imagination, intuition and idealism. Traditionally, though, Jupiter was once credited with this rulership and it is true that most Pisceans are naturally happy, optimistic folk.

Sensitive, sympathetic, impressionable, warm and loving, they seek a harmonious existence and anything brash or vulgar upsets their sensibilities. They are devastated by criticism or unkindness and tend to withdraw into a fantasy world if they encounter either. Some escape in daydreams or lose themselves in books or music; others resort to alcohol, drugs or, as old astrology books describe it, vices of the senses!

Neptune is also the planet of illusion and self-delusion and Pisceans are inclined to ignore or deny problems or difficulties that arise for as long as possible, so self-deception and the deception of those close to them is a common failing. This trait leads, inevitably, to a great deal of confusion and can result in scandal, fraud or intrigue – with the Pisces-born being either perpetrator or victim . . . or both.

Pisces is a dual sign, as symbolised by its glyph: two linked fish swimming in opposite directions, and encompasses the highest human qualities as well as the lowest. Saints and sinners; mystics and misfits; those in need of charity and those who give it; the sick and the imprisoned and those who care for them.

Happily, though, Pisceans are usually well loved and never short of friends because of their kind, gentle natures and endless sympathy for others, particularly those less fortunate than themselves. This is just as well because Pisceans find it hard to imagine anything worse than being unloved for they are the true romantics of the zodiac.

Rather like the couples in fairy tales, Pisceans want their romances to end with the words 'and they lived happily ever after'. Such an idealistic attitude can, of course, lead to disappointment if the loved one is placed on too high a pedestal. Yet, besides their natural charm, compassion and affection, Pisceans are very intuitive and, if they use this latter trait sensibly, stand every chance of finding emotional happiness.

The intuition of Pisceans is a great business asset, too, because it enables them to gauge just the sort of product or service that is needed – and then provide it. This talent rarely lets them down and, even if one or two ideas don't quite come off, they usually manage to make a reasonable living because they are very adaptable and versatile so can usually turn their hand to a variety of activities.

Natural mediums, psychics and healers, many Pisceans are drawn to subjects involving or connected with occultism; others utilise their Neptunian qualities in other ways and shoals of actors and mimics are born under the sign of the Fishes. Music, art and literature also appeal to these gentle people who are genuinely not materialistic despite their natural talent for thinking up money-making schemes. So perhaps we could all learn something from these imaginative, intuitive, idealistic dreamers!

PISCES

Planetary Ruler   NEPTUNE
Element/Quality   WATER/MUTABLE
Keywords   IDEALISM, INTUITION, SENSITIVITY, EMPATHY
Day   THURSDAY
Number   7
Colour   SOFT, SILVERY BLUES AND GREYS
Metal   PLATINUM/TIN
Stones   AQUAMARINE, CHRYSOLITE, CRYSTAL, NEPHRITE
Countries   SAHARA REGION, SUDAN, PORTUGAL, NORMANDY
Places   In Britain: COWES, BOURNEMOUTH, KING'S LYNN, GRIMSBY, LANCASTER, SOUTHPORT, TIVERTON, PRESTON
Elsewhere: ALEXANDRIA, RATISBON, SEVILLE, WORMS
Trees/Shrubs   HAWTHORN, SILVER BIRCH, WILLOW
Flowers/Herbs   COMFREY, LAVENDER, MEADOWSWEET, STONECROP, WILD VIOLET, LICHEN

20 'A man who hates children and dawgs can't be all bad!' whined bibulous comedian/juggler **W. C. Fields** who may have been born today in 1879 but was so secretive that nothing's certain. Another mystery, wealthy **Patty Hearst** (1952) was kidnapped by a group demanding massive charity hand-outs, then brainwashed into joining them.

21 **Jilly Cooper** (1937) before becoming a writer had a variety of jobs including 'puppy fat model' and 'switchboard wrecker' – which seem like Pisces! Hobbies: merry-making, wild flowers, music and mongrels – so do they.
The legless air ace **Douglas Bader** (1910), hero and charity worker for those disabled in a similar way.

22 Scandal today! **Edward Kennedy** (1932) was involved in the tortuous Chappaquiddick incident; **Christine Keeler** (1942) in the Profumo affair.
Comedian **Kenneth Williams** (1926) is volatile – first UP, then down. Always UP, apparently, is **Bruce Forsyth** (1925). Racing driver **Niki Lauda** (1949) sticks to the horizontal but at a great lick.

23 Older birthday gatherers will wish to remember with affection actor **Richard Goolden** (1895) who played Mole in *Wind in the Willows* for donkey's years, and actress **Kathleen Harrison** (1898), usually the harassed Cockney housewife. Younger ones can have **Peter Fonda** (1939) son of Henry, brother of Jane.

24 **Wilhelm Grimm,** one of the brothers who wrote the fairy tales (1786). Staying in the world of poor woodcutters and beautiful princesses, here's **Pat Kirkwood** (1921) formerly a glamorous Principal Boy in never-ending fishnet tights. Also born today, comedienne **Betty Marsden** (1919) who lived on a barge and loves the water.

25 The prolific **Pierre-Auguste Renoir** (1841) painted marshmallow nudes and people enjoying themselves drenched in luminous, rosy, opalescent atmospheres. Golden-voiced tenor **Enrico Caruso** (1877) evokes the Italian sunlight. The voice of **John Arlott** (1914) recalls lazy afternoons spent at the pavilion end.

26 Wealthy businessman **Sir James Goldsmith** (1933) hands out the birthday favours, **Fanny Craddock** bakes the cake, and **Johnny Cash** (1932) sings favourite country-style music, leaving the rest of today's birthday boys and girls to marvel at the exploits of **William Cody,** alias Buffalo Bill (1846).

27 A haul of actresses, all noted for matrimonial entanglements and every one a glamourfish: **Ellen Terry** (1848), **Elizabeth Taylor** (1932) and **Joan Bennett** (1910) whose 'twin' **Lord Cowdray** presides over a business empire reputed to be worth several hundred million pounds in merchant banking and publishing.
Ballerina **Antoinette Sibley** (1939).

28

Rachel (1820) the French tragedienne was born today and twins **Sir John Tenniel** who was the original illustrator of *Alice*. Pisceans don't like being tied down to fact and Alice herself is out of proportion. Nevertheless, she's just right. **Harry H. Corbett** (1925) was just right too for Harold Steptoe.

29

Gioacchino Rossini (1792) boasted that he could set a laundry list to music. Exuberant, volatile and thoroughly likeable, he was married twice and had loads of girl friends. Retired at the height of his fame and spent the last 40 years of his life being a happy gourmet and very, very fat.

1

Pride of place to **Frederic Chopin** (1810).
Glenn Miller (1904) played sweet, romantic music and disappeared in 1944 when flying across the English Channel, a small mystery mightily exaggerated by his countless fans.
David Niven (1910) actor, author and raconteur, was loved by all.
Doris Hare (1905) actress and impersonator.

2

Pat Arrowsmith (1930) was brought up in a religious family. She became a nursing assistant in a mental hospital and a social worker in Liverpool. As a campaigner against nuclear weapons she was imprisoned 10 times, sometimes in solitary confinement. Broadcaster **Jean Metcalfe** (1923) is noted for her sympathetic approach.

3
Glamorous film star **Jean Harlow** (1911) with her waterfall of platinum blonde hair and tight sequinned dresses, trailed scandal through her short, tragic life like one of her silver fox furs. Cartoonist **Ronald Searle** (1920) was a Japanese prisoner of war but survived to introduce us to St Trinians.

4
Voluble astronomer **Patrick Moore** (1927) won't like being in an astrological Birthday Book but it can't be helped.
Pearl White (1889) starred in silent movies *(The Perils of Pauline)*.
Peter Skellern (1947) could set them both to music easily – unless over-awed by sharing his birthday with **Antonio Vivaldi** (1678).

5
Social worker **Lord Beveridge** (1879) wrote a famous Report which became the blueprint for our Welfare State.
Much-married actor **Rex Harrison** (1908) nicknamed Sexy-Rexy – but this is only hearsay as far as the compilers are concerned.
'Twin' TV Fish (1943) – **Jane Rossington** *(Crossroad's* Jill Harvey) and **Hugh Scully.**

6
Humorists include *amazed* **Frankie Howerd** (1922) and **Ring Lardner** (1885) with his sly, gentle art. 'Mother sat facing the front of the train as it makes her giddy to ride backwards. I sat facing her which does not affect me.' Mother was obviously no **Valentina Tereshkova** (1937), first woman astronaut.

7   As a contemporary, the artistic **Lord Snowdon** (1930) will do nicely. As a classic, composer **Maurice Ravel** (1875). He wrote *Pavanne for a Dead Infanta* and *Boléro*. Was very secretive about his music and his sex life, but had much sympathy with children and animals. Loved the antique and exotic.

8   Pisces rules the feet and Fishes either have beautiful trotters like dancing **Cyd Charisse** (1923) and **Lynn Seymour** (1939) or real old plates of meat. Plump, jolly actress **Lynn Redgrave** (1943) *says* she once concussed herself falling over her gym shoes! **Kenneth Graham** (1859) wrote *Wind in the Willows*.

9   *Pisceans,* wrote today's literary Fish, **Peter Quennell** (1905) 'are said to be imaginative and intuitive, and from their ranks spring poets, actors and dancers, people who enjoy variety and movement, abhor monotony and dread boredom,' but they are 'hampered by muddleheadedness that often envelopes them in a dense sub-aqueous fog.'

10   A musical birthday boat. **Owen Brannigan** (1908) the big, bass singer; prima donna **Eva Turner** (1892); Jazz-legend **Bix Beiderbecke** (1903); conductor **Charles Groves** (1915); composer **Arthur Honegger** (1892) and Spanish violinist **Pablo Sarasate** (1844). Swimming alongside **Prince Edward** (1964). Safely on shore, our favourite vet **James Herriot** (1916).

11 Rupert Murdoch (1931) 'the world's most powerful newspaperman' bought the *Sun* and transformed it into a brash tabloid, then the *Times* and *Sunday Times*. International interests include a TV station and an airline.
Stage star **Jessie Matthews** (1907) . . . 3 marriages . . . emotional and volatile . . . insisted on light, colour, harmony and company.

12 First Fish **Liza Minelli** (1946), daugher of Judy Garland, gives the appearance of having come from another world, a fairy-tale world of glitter, glamour and sensation.
Second Fish **Max Wall** (1908) one of our great drolls with that air of pathos which always accompanies classic comedy.

13 **Lafayette Ron Hubbard** (1911) was a fine sci-fi writer who went on to bigger – one can't say better – things and founded Scientology. **Jim Slater** (1929) founded a banking empire valued at £300 million in the 60s and 70s but 'over-reached himself' and collapsed. So watch it!

14 **Albert Einstein** (1879) shows what Pisces is capable of. **Mrs Beeton** (1836), far from being a red-faced old harridan broiling herself and her calves' feet over a kitchener, was an indifferent cook, a beauty and a high-flyer at fashion. Birthday cheer from **Pam Ayres** and **Jasper Carrott** (1945).

15 Bandleader **Harry James** (1916) married frequently. **Lord Melbourne** (1779), Queen Victoria's adored Prime Minster, was – to quote J. B. Priestley – 'a great charmer, an unabashed hedonist who lounged and joked his way into high office and openly loved pleasure and delightful company, especially that of attractive women.'

16 **Patricia Nixon** (1912). Like everyone else around, she was washed away by the Watergate scandal but had been 'Woman of the Year' five times in the USA and was decorated for charitable work.
Leo McKern (1920), actor, portrayer of *Rumpole*, has the fishy hobbies of sailing and swimming.
Teresa Berganza (1936) opera singer.

17 'We Pisceans are very sexy,' says ballet dancer **Rudolph Nureyev** (1937), who knows his astrology. 'Loyal and disloyal, lost in pools and oceans of green water.'
Robin Knox-Johnson (1939) could have been, quite literally, when sailing single-handed round the world.
Artist **Kate Greenaway** (1846) inspired the prettiest children's fashions.

18 Clairvoyant **Edgar Cayce** (1877) diagnosed his clients' ills and prescribed while self-hypnotised. Described their lives in previous existences for good, karmic measure. Whatever they were previously, these entities are now **Mary Malcolm**, former TV announcer; politician **John Silkin** (1923) and lengthy authors **Richard Condon** (1915) and **John Updike** (1932).

19 Explorers **Sir Richard Burton** (1821) and **Dr Livingstone-I-Presume?** (1813). The former was a mystic, linguist and mimic; the latter a missionary. **Tommy Cooper** (1922) is a conjuring clown; **Ursula Andress** (1936) a beauty; and **Baroness Vetsera** (1871) is tragic – she was shot at Meyerling by her lover, Prince Rudolph.

20 The medium **Daniel Dunglas Home** was born today in 1833. The famous of the day attended his séances and the lucky ones saw him float out of one window and in at the next. 'His history presents a curious and, as yet, unsolved problem,' muses the Dictionary of National Biography.

21 Away, that month despicable,
  those days of dread and doubt,
When the gale blows down the chimney,
  and the oil is running out.
Besides, I own a private cause to
  call the time accurst –
I'll have another birthday when
  It's March the twenty-first!
        Phyllis McGinley (1905)
        American humorist.

NOTES